George Moore was considered during his lifetime to have been one of the supreme masters of prose style in the early years of this century, and he was renowned for rewriting his books as his style developed. His many famous works include *Hail and Farewell!*, *The Lake*, *A Drama in Muslin* (rewritten as *Muslin*), *Evelyn Innes*, *Esther Waters*, *The Brook Kerith* and *A Story Teller's Holiday*, though many would immediately call to mind others of his *oeuvre*.

Moore died in January 1933 and this collection is gathered together to celebrate the fiftieth anniversary of his death. The essays (in order of appearance in the book) are 'George Moore, A Reappraisal' (Janet Egleson Dunleavy), 'Moore Hall, 1952' (Richard J. Byrne), 'George Moore's Paris' (Jane Crisler), 'George Moore's Dublin' (James Liddy), 'Private Moore, Public Moore' (Robert Stephen Becker), 'George Moore's Medievalism' (Gareth W. Dunleavy), 'The Moore-Joyce Nexus' (Patrick A. McCarthy), 'George Moore and Samuel Beckett' (Melvin J. Friedman), 'Collecting Moore' (Edwin Gilcher). To these are a collection of 17 portraits, in life and caricature, of George Moore, and an Appendix, 'Some Bibliographical Notes' by Edwin Gilcher in which he adds to the information he published in his *A Bibliography of George Moore* (1970).

appear shortly. A 1984 Guggenheim Fellow, she is now collaborating with Gareth W. Dunleavy on a biography of Douglas Hyde.

GEORGE MOORE IN PERSPECTIVE

GEORGE MOORE IN PERSPECTIVE

Edited by
Janet Egleson Dunleavy

Irish Literary Studies 16

1983

MALTON PRESS   COLIN SMYTHE
Naas, County Kildare   Gerrards Cross, Bucks

BARNES & NOBLE BOOKS
Totowa, New Jersey

Copyright © 1983 by Janet Egleson Dunleavy, Richard J. Byrne, Jane Crisler,
James Liddy, Robert Stephen Becker, Gareth W. Dunleavy, Patrick A. McCarthy,
Melvin J. Friedman, Edwin Gilcher
Unpublished letters by George Moore copyright © 1983 John Christopher Medley

The collection first published in 1983
by Colin Smythe Limited, Gerrards Cross, Buckinghamshire
and The Malton Press Ltd., Monread Road, Naas, Co. Kildare

British Library Cataloguing in Publication Data

George Moore in perspective.—(Irish literary studies,
ISSN 0140–895X; 16)
1. Moore, George, 1852–1933—Criticism and
interpretation
I. Dunleavy, Janet Egleson   II. Series
823′.8   PR5043

ISBN 0–86140–120–4 (Colin Smythe Ltd.)
ISBN 0–905261–12–7 (The Malton Press Ltd.)

First published in the United States of America in 1983
by Barnes & Noble Books, 81 Adams Drive, Totowa, N.J.07512

Library of Congress Cataloging in Publication Data
Main entry under title:

George Moore in perspective.

(Irish literary studies, ISSN 0140–895X ; 16)
Bibliography: p.
Includes index.
1. Moore, George, 1852–1933—Addresses, essays,
lectures. 2. Authors, Irish—19th century—Biography—
Addresses, essays, lectures. I. Dunleavy, Janet
Egleson. II. Series.
PR5043.G46 1983   823′.8   83–3722
ISBN 0–389–20395–5

Printed in Great Britain
Typeset by Inforum Ltd, Portsmouth and printed and bound
by Billing & Sons Ltd, Worcester

CONTENTS

ILLUSTRATIONS

between pages 80 and 81

MAPS

GEORGE MOORE: A REAPPRAISAL[1]

JANET EGLESON DUNLEAVY

Fifty years ago, on 21 January 1933, George Moore died. In Ireland, England, the United States, and France, his death was a significant event: for almost fifty years George Moore, novelist, essayist, and raconteur, had been a household name. Eleven months before, on 24 February 1932, members of the leading intellectual, artistic, and literary circles of England, Ireland, and France had joined Ramsay MacDonald, then Prime Minister of England, in paying homage to George Moore. They addressed, they had declared,

an artist who, since he came to London . . ., has not ceased to labour with a single mind in the perfecting of his craft, who has written in *Daphnis and Chloë* a flawless translation, in *Esther Waters* a tale that marks a period in our literature, in *Hail and Farewell* an autobiography that has rank with Rousseau's, in *Héloïse and Abélard* a philosophical romance of supreme beauty, and in *The Brook Kerith* a prose epic unique in the English language.

Moore's eightieth birthday had been the occasion for this memorial; his achievement, as documented by those who had addressed him, was its reason:

The uses of that language have been changed by your influence, as though in an ancient music you had discovered new melodies and rhythms that shall be in the air when young men in future time have stories to tell. You have taught narrative to flow again and anecdote to illumine it as the sun a stream. You have persuaded words and invention to sing new songs together that would have been heard, as those of an equal, by the masters upon whom the tradition of our literature relies, and on your eightieth birthday your pen is still unfailing in your hand. For these reasons we salute you. . . .

The following morning, 25 February 1932, the full text of their tribute, complete with signatures, was published in the London *Times*. Deeply affected by this unprecedented recognition of an author's work, by such praise of his craft from so many influential colleagues and contemporaries, George Moore 'thought a great deal . . . of the pleasure it would be . . . to spend three or four weeks writing letters' to those who had honoured him. But his pen was 'still unfailing' in his hand; the manuscript of a story to be entitled 'Madeleine de Lisle' was unfinished. 'The thread of a story is easily broken and . . . characters grow dim if they are allowed to lie dormant in the imagination', he explained, in his answer addressed to the *Times* and published on 1 March 1932; 'I feel sure that my friends and the signatories to the memorial would forego the pleasure of receiving letters of thanks if, by so doing, they would help me to write my book, which I trust they will like'.

As had Keats before him, Moore feared that he might cease to be before his pen had gleaned his teeming brain: beyond 'Madeleine de Lisle' – a tale woven of 'high cloudy symbols of a high romance', in the style Moore favoured in his last years – his imagination held other shadows he wished to trace. His fears were realized. On 21 January 1933 'Madeleine de Lisle' was left incomplete. Although published posthumously, so was *A Communication to My Friends*, for Moore considered it to be still a work-in-progress at the time of his death. Its manuscript drafts did not satisfy him: they lacked, he complained, that correction of form that is virtue (an imperative Moore had borrowed from Théophile Gautier); to him, it was not yet a 'virtuous' book. With Oscar Wilde, a friend out of his Mayo boyhood, George Moore believed in virtue as necessary in literature, if not in life. For him, as for Wilde, the morality of art consisted in 'the perfect use of an imperfect medium'.

The correction of form, the perfection of use of an imperfect medium: these were the concepts that were central to the aesthetic theories of George Moore throughout his life. For him they defined artistic purpose; for his contemporaries they underscored his achievement. Thus Moore the literary artist was never satisfied. He experimented constantly with form, style, and method of presenting character; he was accused of conducting his education in public, book by book. But correction of form and the perfect use of an imperfect medium were the concepts that provided the underlying unity of Moore's aesthetic: they integrated the artistic ideas he incorporated into his work.

Prominent among the ideas to which Moore remained fully and consistently committed throughout his writing career was that the arts are interrelated – that aesthetic theories developed by a composer have meaning for painters and writers; that artistic truths perceived by a writer illumine music and painting; that artistic forms devised by a painter give shape also to both literature and music. Of these three means of transmitting artistic perception – through music, through painting, through literature – Moore himself had begun with painting. His formal aesthetic training from 1870 to 1876 had been in the visual arts; from the visual arts (for which in 1876 he decided he had no real talent, an opinion not shared by colleagues who knew his work), Moore turned to writing. His earliest essays were written about art; his earliest creative writings were attempts to produce through words the visual art of drama. An early achievement was the book of a light opera, *Les Cloches de Corneville* – a successful marriage of words and music on which he had collaborated with his brother Augustus. Predictably, when Moore turned to poetry, he composed in imitation of Baudelaire and the French symbolists (he understood sinesthesia not as a concept but as an experience). Edouard Dujardin, who in his long career was editor of both *La Révue Wagnerienne* and the companion periodical, *La Révue Independente*, associated with the symbolists, was the close friend from whom Moore learned the techniques of literary Wagnerism. As an artistic idea literary Wagnerism was compatible with similar ideas practised with shape and colour which Moore had seen in French painting, in the works of artists to whom he had been introduced in the cafés of the Left Bank and Montmartre.

George Moore's early experience in art was determined, however, not by the French fashions of his young manhood but by the country, class, and century into which he had been born and by the tastes of his father, George Henry Moore, an English-educated Irish-Catholic landowner and Member of Parliament, master of Moore Hall in County Mayo.[2] The Moores claimed descent from Sir Thomas More; they were kin to Lord Sligo; they had lived abroad, in comfort, during the Penal times that had destroyed the fortunes of less fortunate Irish-Catholic families; they had been received by the king and queen of Spain. In architectural style and furnishings Moore Hall reflected the Moore family history and George Henry Moore's place in fashionable society. Nineteenth-century fashionable society favoured classical scenes and large historical paintings: oversize historical canvasses hung at Moore Hall; sculptured mermen and mermaids supported the intricately carved mantel-piece of its oak-panelled dining room; the decorative panels of its drawing room employed motifs adapted from Greek classical art. Among George Henry Moore's friends and acquaintances were members of the Pre-Raphaelite Brotherhood, the 'moderns' of the period in which George Moore grew up, who became popular and respectable after they received the support of John Ruskin. George Henry Moore's own tastes followed the dictates of the Royal Academy, for whom classical art provided the standards by which contemporary artists were judged. Often he took his two older sons – George, who became the novelist, Maurice, who became an Army officer and an Irish senator – to exhibitions, where he lectured them on neo-classical painting and sculpture. George Henry Moore died when young George was but eighteen; at the insistence of mother and uncles, who would not permit him to go to Paris, George began his study of drawing and painting at the South Kensington Museum, under instructors who shared George Henry Moore's ideas about art. Through his father's friends he gained admission to fine homes in Kensington, where he could see original Rossettis. During this period he also visited often the studio of a kinsman, Jim Browne, who had painted one of the historical canvasses that hung at Moore Hall ('The Burial of the Indian Chief', it was called) and who had had a painting accepted by the Royal Academy.

In 1873 George Moore turned twenty-one. He was of age; he was master of Moore Hall; he no longer had to accept the restrictions or heed the caveats of mother and uncles. He had a young man's yearning for adventure, for change, for identification with a new order that would replace the old. Paris beckoned: it was, he had been told, the cradle of new ideas in art, ideas that were even more 'modern' than those of the Pre-Raphaelites. He went to France. Yet he was cautious; in Paris he sought instruction not from the radicals but from, as he wrote to his mother, 'trained artists': Cabanel, Lefebvre, Gerôme, Meissonier. He concentrated on technique. In English studios pupils were taught to outline figures; in French ateliers they learned to construct the human body using dioramic shapes, some light, some shadowed. After he had been in Paris for a year, Moore returned to a studio in Cromwell Mews, in London, where he painted women in the style of Rossetti. He was introduced to James MacNeill Whistler, whom he later acknowledged he could not help but admire. A few months later he again went to France, where he remained, except for brief visits to England and Ireland, until he was almost thirty. There he listened to talk of Delacroix's ability as a colourist; of the French painters who had set up their easels out-of-doors and painted shadows in complementary colours; and of a new brash school of French painters who did not measure a figure in terms of seven and a half heads, cared nothing if a drawing of a human arm violated precepts of balance and order, and dismissed, against all convention, logic, and wisdom, such criticism as 'il n'est porte pas'. Even after he concluded that he himself would not become an artist, Moore continued to listen to talk of painting and sculpture, leaving studio instruction for the different kind of training he could receive in the cafés of Paris, especially the Nouvelles Athènes, where ideas were exchanged not only by Renoir, Sisley, Monet, Pissarro, and Morisot, but also by Edmond Goncourt, Turgenev, and Zola. In the Nouvelles Athènes he found new idols: Degas, Manet. Degas was reticent, but Manet invited Moore to visit his Rue de St. Petersbourg studio, where he asked the young Irishman to sit for his portrait. The result, painted in the new French fashion, was the pastel that hangs today in the permanent collection of the Metropolitan Museum in New York: the eyes are as blue as cornflowers, the straw-coloured hair and beard are unruly, the mouth is slightly open, as if about to ask the question implied by the expression in the eyes. Very different from the portraits Moore had been taught to paint in London, in the South Kensington Museum, when he was eighteen, it captures Moore not in the period of his youth but at a single moment of a single day of his youthful years.

Moore's early unsuccessful attempts to write for the stage belong to these years, when his academy was the Nouvelles Athènes. Diminished rent receipts from Moore Hall soon encouraged him to seek more successful outlets for his writing efforts: he began to publish articles and reviews – mostly about contemporary art and artists, but also about theatre and literature – for English readers. In addition, he wrote two volumes of poetry that were published in England under titles reminiscent of Baudelaire: *Flowers of Passion* and *Pagan Poems*. These did not earn him money but they did help to establish a certain kind of reputation which Moore later delighted in exploiting. In London, to which he was forced to move, as a result of reductions in his income, he became known as 'Pagan Moore', a young Irishman who sometimes would lapse into French when he was speaking, as though he had forgotten his English, and who talked easily and well about French art. Very likely it was the style of his life rather than the style of his writing that attracted the little attention given to his first novel, *A Modern Lover*, when it appeared in 1883. Critics suggested that there might be a certain autobiographical quality in the content of the novel, which was about a young artist whose gradual climb to fame, wealth, and social position was accomplished not through hard work or even talent but at the expense of three women. Its plot was obviously designed to appeal to popular reading tastes: the nineteenth century dearly loved a cad.

Beyond plot, however, *A Modern Lover* offers a dialogue about modern art – even as, structurally, it reveals a classical balance of elements: the story of Gwynnie Lloyd, a fellow roomer in a cheap lodging house, who divests herself of both honour and clothing to pose nude for Lewis when she discovers that he cannot afford to pay a model, is told in the opening pages; it is retold at the conclusion. In the first three chapters of volume one, Gwynnie passes out of Lewis's life; in the final three chapters of volume one, Lady Helen, a willful young lady of high social position, enters it. Between these episodes Lewis meets Lucy Bentham, an older woman with a substantial income, separated from her husband, who begins by mothering Lewis, underwrites his training in Paris, and becomes his patron and then his mistress. Volume two begins with Lewis leaving Mrs Bentham to go to Paris. They are reunited; the volume ends with his leaving Mrs Bentham to go to Lady Helen, who has agreed to marry him despite her family's opposition. Gwynnie, unrecognized, disfigured by smallpox, returns to the narrative in volume three, as Lady Helen's maid. She collapses when she hears whom her mistress is to marry. The marriage takes place, happily for Lewis, because Lady Helen uses her connexions and influence to force her husband's undeserved election to the Royal Academy; unhappily for Lady Helen, for she soon learns that to her husband she is but another stepping stone in his path to success. In each volume the narrative is interrupted at midpoint by a discussion of the conflict between opposing schools of art.

Visual descriptions of the characters of *A Modern Lover* are drawn from painting, not life. As a young woman, Gwynnie poses for Lewis's painting of Venus rising from the sea, tossing her hair about her body – an obvious imitation of the Botticelli that Moore used to admire on his visits with his father to the National Gallery, when he was a boy. Disfigured by smallpox at the end of the novel, she is the poor working woman painted in squalid surroundings by such artists as Degas, Jean Francois Millet, and Clausen. Lady Helen is, according to two minor characters, 'very Greek' in appearance; descriptive passages make clear that the reference is to Greek art. She has a 'classical beauty', she is like a statue, she is immaculately white, with a certain hardness or coldness, she is 'the type of all that is elegant'. Lucy Bentham is tall, a Pre-Raphaelite subject, with abundant hair and bosom. As seen in Bendish's gallery, Mr Bendish and Lewis present a contrast of romantic, picturesque portraiture on the one hand and classical, academic portraiture on the other. Mr Bendish is 'an old, wizened little creature, with a grizzled white beard'; Lewis is 'a young man of exquisite beauty, his feminine grace . . . like a relic of ancient

Greece'. Mr Bendish's gallery, with its dark corners, draperies, and clutter, also is described as if it were a romantic painting. It contrasts with Mrs Bentham's ballroom, in which cornices and mouldings appear to be of white marble (actually they have been modelled in plaster of Paris, following Greek examples). On the wall panels there are 'Venuses and Cupids to no end; flowers, tendrils, grapes, all kinds of fruit in profusion', executed in the manner of Boucher, Watteau, and other artists admired by the academicians.

Debates about art in *A Modern Lover* are between the academicians on the one hand, the artists who dominated the Royal Academy, and those Moore calls the 'moderns' on the other. Allied with the former are the medievalists, who reject classical standards yet support the Academy against the moderns. The group that styles itself 'modern' is made up not only of artists, although they are its leaders, but also of composers and writers. Their common belief, reminiscent of Zola, is that the arts, which are interrelated, are 'the issue of the manners and customs of the day, and change with those manners according to a general law'. Analogies between this group and the circle at the Nouvelles Athènes are obvious, although the former is presented as English. Fraser's theories and subjects, for example, are like those of Monet, who experimented with atmospheric effects and painted *Le Gare St. Lazare à Paris*. Thompson's theories are similar to those Moore later attributed to Degas, in *Impressions and Opinions*. Any one of three, Renoir, Manet, or Berthe Morisot (or a composite of all three), might have chosen the bright colours and subject of the picnic party painted in the novel by Crossley. Like Manet, Crossley also painted racehorses. Despite these resemblances, it is not certain that Moore intended to use the circle of the Nouvelles Athènes in his fiction: he specifically denied the connexion between the moderns of *A Modern Lover* and the French impressionists in an article published in *Hawk* in December, 1889. According to Moore, the ideas expressed by his moderns were 'in the air' of London at the time. Jacques-Émile Blanche, Moore's friend and a young contemporary, supported this assertion: such an informal group, he declared, did exist in England in the 1870s. Many were Moore's friends and acquaintances; some he had met through his father; some he had known as an art student in South Kensington or later, at Barthe's classes; some had been for brief periods members of the English colony in Dieppe and Paris. Many had been rejected by the Academy because of their unorthodox opinions. These were the painters who formed the nucleus of the Grosvenor Gallery exhibitions a few years later. Little known in France, according to

Jacques-Émile Blanche, they had little recognition in England until the World Exhibition of 1878. The pivotal exhibition in *A Modern Lover* is dated 1879.

Moore's second novel, *A Mummer's Wife* (1884), belongs to the period when Moore styled himself *'un ricochet de Zola'* in England. Critics also have noted the influence of Flaubert. Indeed, the central character, Kate Ede, is a kind of Madame Bovary. Her husband is a linen draper; they live in a factory town; through the landlady of her childhood Kate has been exposed to popular romantic literature. An acting company comes to town, and Kate quickly succumbs to the attempts of Dick Lennox, who boards with the Edes, to seduce her. She runs away with him, goes on stage herself, takes to drink, and eventually dies, a coarse, unlovely skeleton of her former self.

A Mummer's Wife is developed pictorially, through a series of related scenes. Each scene takes Kate for its primary subject; each shows her struggling with one of the deadly sins. Descriptive passages invite comparison with engravings popular in the Victorian era that dramatized struggles with vice and virtue. These were the wall decorations of the Ede household. Like the scenes engraved by Burne-Jones and George Frederick Watts, those described in *A Mummer's Wife* could have been titled *Hope*, *Youth*, *Love and Death*, *Life's Illusion*, and *Sic Transit*. In structure, however, *A Mummer's Wife* has the same classical balance as *A Modern Lover*: for Kate Ede, the narrow base of a meager factory-town existence broadens into a fullness that includes life with a sophisticated man, the admiration of crowds, fine clothing, money; it then narrows again to wretchedness, poverty, illness, and death. All is proportionate: ten chapters are devoted to each of the three phases of Kate's story.

An interesting technique adapted from theories of art is introduced in *A Mummer's Wife*. Following the idea that 'nature abhors a straight line', all that is natural and beautiful is curving and sinuous, all that is artificial and ugly is angular. Occasionally (but in this novel not yet consistently), Moore manipulates the narrative consciousness through which he filters his story to shift focus from object perceived to mind of perceiver: the factory town is angular by day; at night, its sharp angles appear softer and rounder as reality fades, chores are set aside, and Kate is able to turn inward, to the life of her imagination. Beyond the factory town, there is always the curve of sky and of surrounding hills, promising that the beauty that preceded the building of the ugly town will outlast it. As in *A Modern Lover*, the characters of *A Mummer's Wife* are described as if painted: they are figures out of portraits and landscapes. But Kate is presented as a young woman in a passage that represents an advance in technique for Moore. Focusing not on the visual impression received by a viewer of an impressionist painting but on the palette and technique of the painter, he describes her complexion as 'filled with the delicate green of an ostrich egg, and modelled as delicately'. Unfortunately, this passage is not successful: the reader cannot be trusted to see with a painter's eye; the mind does not admire green-skinned beauty. In later novels Moore was more careful in his choice of colours while employing the same technique.

By the time Moore published his third novel, *A Drama in Muslin* (1886), he had learned to write descriptive passages more skillfully. References to styles of painting and specific artists still abound, requiring that a reader be familiar with eighteenth- and nineteenth-century European painting to 'see' Moore's characters as he presents them, but in landscapes and group scenes, especially in ballroom scenes, there is more verbal brushwork. Relying less on his reader's memory, more on his reader's visual imagination, Moore recreates rather than refers to such details as how the textures of silks, satins, and velvets may be distinguished visually and the ways in which different fabrics absorb candlelight. In his next novel he continues to employ the painterly techniques introduced in *A Drama in Muslin*; in addition, he matches character and colour, choosing tints and shades not only for their pictorial qualities but also for their associational values. Thus John Norton of *A Mere Accident* (1887), a young aesthete, lives in a mauve and yellow world, yearning for the white radiance of eternity. In *Mike Fletcher* (1889), Moore's seventh novel, Moore makes further use of the abstract potential of descriptive passages, using colour and style to create a psychological portrait and to underline correspondences between inner and outer reality. The external world changes in appearance in response to the mood of the character in focus as, in painting, objects perceived change in appearance in response to changing light. Although *Esther Waters* (1894) is often discussed as an example of English naturalism and Moore himself insisted that it was based on the kind of notebook observation of reality he had learned from Zola, a comparison of this 'English novel' (actually indebted in both landscape and character to Moore's Mayo) with *A Mummer's Wife* reveals how much Moore's style had changed in the decade that separates them. Esther comes to Woodview, to work for Mrs Barfield, in the springtime of her life and the springtime of the year; she is reunited with Mrs Barfield at Woodview in the autumn of her life:

descriptive passages leave no doubt about the connexion between setting and subject. But there the novel does not end; it continues through to February, to talk of fixing up the garden and sowing vegetables, to Esther's observations that already the land has the gray-green look of early spring. Her son, a handsome young soldier, comes up the avenue to greet her; in the repetition of the opening lines there is both a conclusion and a new beginning. From beginning to end, Esther's character changes as slowly and as imperceptibly as the seasons, through incremental repetition of minute detail.

With the publication of *The Untilled Field* (1903), Moore began a new century with a new style, developed from the experiments in his earlier work: sound and rhythm were introduced to enhance visual imagery. In the novels of his later years – *The Lake*, *The Brook Kerith*, *Héloïse and Abélard*, *Aphrodite in Aulis* – the imperfect medium he wished to perfect through art became the subjective reality of the visible world. This was reality as it was understood by the impressionists and postimpressionists, created on the page and then recreated in the mind of the reader through both harmony and cacaphony of sound, line, and colour, as the text required. In these last works Moore showed that he had learned to combine the perceptions of composer, painter, and writer as he painted with words; he had found ways to make the idea of the interrelationship of the arts serve his own artistic purpose.[3]

Unfortunately, since Moore's death in 1933, there have been few attempts to understand his theories of literary art or trace his artistic development. Most studies have focused on the author himself or have attempted to examine his art through the mind and heart of the artist. To be sure, the George Moore who is most accessible to critics is irresistible: he is flamboyant, unconventional, iconoclastic, eccentric, a lover of anecdotes (especially those in which he plays a major role). He is self-aggrandizing, self-dramatizing, tactless, dishonest when honesty would ruin a choice bit of gossip, witty, articulate, excellent at repartee. If we believe Susan Mitchell, he is a man of few actions but many words: some men kiss and tell, she declares, but George Moore only tells. Old mocker, he loved best to mock himself. What did it matter what a Susan Mitchell might say? Challenged as to the accuracy of his account of an incident involving a woman, Moore would declare that truth was unimportant – the tale was worth the telling if it made a good story. If it made a good story, he would mislead willingly those who would listen, even when he talked about himself as *cavaliere servente* to his favourite mistress, art. Because it made a good story, he often described himself as virtually uneducated, an artist manqué, a foolish poseur, a chameleon, a man of wax. In moral England where everything French was regarded as by definition immoral, he delighted in presenting himself as a disciple of Baudelaire and Zola, a rake who had studied debauchery in Paris. When his fifth novel, *Confessions of a Young Man* (1888), was called autobiographical, he obligingly changed the name of its central character from Edward Dayne to George Moore. In Ireland, in a Dublin rediscovering its Irish heritage, he alternated between publicly declaring himself a true Gael who henceforth would publish only in Irish (a language he did not know) and publicly renouncing his Irish Catholicism in favour of the Church of England.

George Moore as created by George Moore had unity of being, consistency of character, symmetry of style. Durable, unchanging, predictable in his idiosyncracies, he was a true work of art: his idiosyncracies shocked and instructed; their predictability entertained. By contrast, as Graham Hough has observed, to understand the canon of George Moore requires 'a panoramic view of the formation of a taste and attitude, of all the various aesthetic and social influences that helped to shape it'.[4] Malcolm Brown has described Moore's career as 'an incomparable aesthetic journey, ranging more widely than the careers of Shaw, or Bennett, or Wells, or even Joyce or Yeats'.[5] In 1901 a sophomoric James Joyce, writing 'The Day of the Rabblement', dismissed Moore's experiments in technique as 'struggling in the backwash of that tide which has advanced from Flaubert through Jakobsen to D'Annunzio . . .'; later, having accorded Moore that sincerest form of flattery, imitation (witness the echoes of Moore's *Confessions* in *A Portrait of the Artist as a Young Man*), a mature Joyce affixed his signature to the memorial honouring Moore on his eightieth birthday.[6]

Four problems confront serious students of Moore's work. The first is that of separating the persona of the author, a work of art, from the author himself. This is a difficult task that requires abjuring all fascinating anecdotes, whether told by Moore himself, or validated by friend or brother, or declared authentic by an enemy, or inscribed for future generations in one of Moore's so-called memoirs or autobiographies. All Moore's memoirs and autobiographies blend fact and fiction: they are works of art for which the author sat. More reliable (and often more informative) is Moore's correspondence. For example, available letters (a comprehensive collection, edited by Robert S. Becker, will be published shortly) did prove useful to both Helmut Gerber and

Edwin Gilcher in establishing certain facts concerning the author and his craft. Joseph Hone's biography is useful also in ascertaining facts of Moore's life and in presenting the broad outlines of his milieu: it has the usual limitations of a life of the body; art has its genesis in the life of the mind. To evoke the life of the mind, especially a mind like George Moore's, energized by qualities in opposition and engaged in the exploration of subjective reality, Moore himself offered advice: study the form of each work; compare the author's treatment of each theme with the ways in which others have treated similar themes. Among those who have written about Moore both Malcolm Brown (*George Moore: A Reconsideration*) and Richard Cave (*A Study of the Novels of George Moore*) have attempted to follow Moore's advice, the one focusing on theme, the other comparing Moore with others of similar artistic persuasion. If Brown, perplexed by Moore's changing style, concluded by diagnosing him as suffering from 'aesthetic schizophrenia', no doubt Brown's disadvantage was that he worked without the benefit later scholars enjoyed of being able to consult Edwin Gilcher's clarifying notes to his *Bibliography* or Helmut Gerber's commentary in *George Moore in Transition*. Cave's limited speculations are understandable, for his central purpose was to study character and motivation in the novels.

The second problem confronting the serious student of Moore is that of subdividing and labelling the author's canon. What, for example, should be done with the memoirs and autobiographical writings that weave together fact and fiction? Are *Confessions of a Young Man* and *Hail and Farewell* novels, or autobiographies, or both, or neither? Moore himself described them as works of fiction, but many critics – for persuasive reasons – do not accept his statements. And what of *Memoirs of My Dead Life*? Rupert Hart-Davis calls its 'the first autobiographical book that Moore wrote after 1894', yet acknowledges that 'each time a new edition gave him the opportunity', Moore 'rewrote parts of the book extensively, adding or removing whole sections, so that it is necessary to consult every edition from 1906 to 1928 to find all the references to his love for Lady Cunard'.[7] Furthermore, Hart-Davis acknowledges that if these references are accepted as autobiographical, the differences among them must be reconciled, for Moore transposed 'dates, events, and people in any way that suited his artistic purpose'. Nevertheless, Hart-Davis insists that 'the more one studies the books in conjunction with the known incidents of Moore's life, the more certainly do even the most outrageous anecdotes appear to rest on a substratum of fact'. Is a 'substratum of fact' sufficient to distinguish *Memoirs* as an autobiographical book rather than a work of fiction? The question is valid, for many other authors also have used known incidents from their lives to provide a substratum of fact in works labelled fiction: e.g., Tennessee Williams, *The Glass Menagerie*, and James Joyce, *A Portrait of the Artist as a Young Man*. At the same time, many have taken imaginative liberties with facts in works labelled nonfiction, e.g., Thoreau's *Walden*, Henry James's *The Middle Years*. The number of Moore's works in doubt as to classification is significant: in addition to *Confessions*, *Memoirs*, and *Hail and Farewell*, it includes *Avowals*, *Conversations on Ebury Street*, and *A Communication to My Friends* – each, with the exception of the last, revised each time it was republished. The question is further complicated by letters, introductions, and prefaces by the author in which still other versions of the 'known incidents' of his life are sketched.

The third problem confronting the serious student of Moore's work concerns his revisions. Quoting Moore's confession that he was 'a victim of the disease of rewriting', Richard Cave notes that, like his autobiographical writings, 'few of his novels escaped revision; several underwent wholesale redrafting'.[8] The most serious effects of this disease have been suffered not by the afflicted author but by students of his work. Before publication in 1970 of Edwin Gilcher's *Bibliography*, anyone undertaking a study of either a single work or Moore's entire canon faced enormous difficulties in establishing the number and sequence of revised texts. Errors and omissions were almost unavoidable. Yet, as Gilcher points out, to understand the art of George Moore – to follow Moore's aesthetic journey and then stand back for that 'panoramic view of the formation of a taste and attitude' recommended by Graham Hough – it is necessary to examine the ways in which the correction of form produced significantly different versions of the same literary work. 'If you wish to estimate the true value of an author's art', advised Moore, 'study his revisions'. Lionel Stevenson's introduction, notes, and appendices to the Riverside Edition (1963) of *Esther Waters* provide an example of the value of Moore's advice. Susan Dick's variorum edition of *Confessions of a Young Man* (1971) is another major contribution to this aspect of Moore studies. Both owe a debt to the pioneer essay, 'George Moore's Revisions of *The Lake*, 'The Wild Goose', and *Esther Waters*', in which Royal A. Gettman called attention to Moore's habits of revision.[9] Additional efforts of this kind are needed, not only to reveal more about the development of a single work but also to provide a basis for determining how George Moore applied his aesthetic theories at different stages of his long and unusually varied writing career.

The fourth problem that confronts the serious student who undertakes a study of George Moore is that of tracing his wide-ranging aesthetic journey, both for its influence on his own writing and for whatever significance it may have had to others. Some stages of this journey have been examined: Georges-Paul Collet, Walter D. Ferguson, and Jean C. Noel have analyzed and written about the intellectual and cultural influences Moore absorbed during the years he spent in France;[10] Robert Porter Sechler has discussed Moore as a disciple of Walter Pater;[11] Sonja Nejdefors-Frisk has focussed on George Moore's naturalistic prose;[12] Graham Hough has examined Moore's literary response to the 1890s;[13] I have suggested some ways in which Moore's early commitment to painting and his lifelong interest in the visual arts shaped his aesthetic theories and directed the development of his craft.[14]

To mark the fiftieth anniversary of Moore's death, five of the contributors to this volume have continued the work of tracing Moore's aesthetic journey. Each has followed different avenues. Richard Byrne has recreated George Moore's Mayo from both the visible and the invisible evidence he stored in his memory on first exploring Moore Hall and the surrounding countryside in 1952, the 100th anniversary of Moore's birth; among his observations was the fact that time has brought few changes to both the rhythm of life and the insularity of existence described in Moore's fiction. Jane Crisler, comparing and contrasting the political and social climate of the Paris Moore knew in the 1870s and the Dublin and London to which he returned in the 1880s, explains the role he would have been assigned by the French, as a young Irishman of means, and offers new insights into Moore's subsequent attitudes and behavior. James Liddy, noting how each of Ireland's major writers has left as a legacy the Dublin he knew, evokes Moore's Dublin of 1901–1911, the significant growing years of the Irish Literary Renaissance. Drawing on both personal and professional correspondence, Robert Stephen Becker recreates the features of two dichotomous George Moores, the one private, the other public, as each was known to his Dublin and London worlds. These literary portraits are supplemented by a rare group of illustrations, captioned by Professor Becker. Gareth W. Dunleavy explores at last a subject that has long fascinated Moore scholars – the extent of Moore's knowledge of medieval literature, the sources of his knowledge, and the ways in which he made use of it.

Three of the contributors examine George Moore from a

different perspective. Patrick A. McCarthy documents the often discussed Moore-Joyce nexus. Melvin J. Friedman investigates the cross-currents and correspondences that link George Moore and Samuel Beckett. Edwin Gilcher, the acknowledged expert on all questions related to the George Moore canon, explains why George Moore has become a favourite of book collectors – and what new collectors should look for if they are just beginning to build a George Moore library.

An appendix contains Edwin Gilcher's first published bibliographical notes, correcting and supplementing (on the basis of information brought to light since 1970) *A Bibliography of George Moore*, itself the result of more than thirty years of research.

NOTES

1   A brief early version of this essay was presented at the 1979 Annual Meeting of the Modern Language Association of America, San Francisco. For many of the observations included here I have drawn also on my study of Moore's development as a literary artist, *George Moore: The Artist's Vision, the Storyteller's Art* (Lewisburg, Pennsylvania: Bucknell University Press, 1973).
2   Like all students of Moore's work, I am indebted chiefly to Joseph Hone, *The Life of George Moore* (New York: Macmillan, 1936) and *The Moores of Moore Hall* (London: Cape, 1939), and to Maurice Moore, *An Irish Gentleman: George Henry Moore* (London: T. Werner Laurie [1913]) for biographical data and information about the Moore family background. For information about specific phases of Moore's life, I have drawn also (with caution, because he so frequently mixes fact and fiction) on Moore's own purportedly non-fictional writings and on Georges-Paul Collet, *George Moore et la France* (Paris and Geneva: Librairie E. Droz and Librairie Minard, 1957); Jacques-Émile Blanche, *Portraits of a Lifetime*, tr. Walter Clement (New York: Coward-McCann, 1938); John Freeman, *A Portrait of George Moore in a Study of his Work* (London: T. Werner Laurie, 1922); Frank Harris, *Contemporary Portraits*, 2nd Series (New York: privately printed, 1919); Desmond MacCarthy, *Portraits* (London: Putnam, 1932); and Jean C. Noel, *George Moore: l'Homme et l'Oeuvre (1852–1922)*, Études Anglaises 24 (Paris: Didier, 1966). Although it was compiled with the primary purpose of providing bibliographic information, I have found Edwin Gilcher's *A Bibliography of George Moore* (DeKalb, Illinois: Northern Illinois University Press, 1970) to be exceedingly useful in clearing up contradictions in the biographical studies, especially those related to date and circumstance of composition and publication. I have consulted also Moore's accounts of his work in his published correspondence, chiefly in *Letters to Dujardin* (New York: Crosby Gaige, 1929); *Letters of George Moore* [to John Eglinton] (Bournemouth: privately printed, 1942); *Letters to Lady Cunard*, ed. Rupert Hart-Davis (London: Rupert Hart-Davis, 1957); and *George Moore in Transition*, ed. Helmut E. Gerber (Detroit: Wayne State University Press, 1968). Also of interest to me,

in making this reappraisal, have been three studies: Malcolm Brown, *George Moore: A Reconsideration* (Seattle: University of Washington Press, 1955); Richard Cave, *A Study of the Novels of George Moore* (Gerrard's Cross: Colin Smythe, Ltd. and New York: Barnes & Noble, 1978); and Anthony Farrow, *George Moore* (Boston, Twayne Publishers, 1978). In addition, there are two collections of essays that I would recommend to others: Douglas A. Hughes, ed., *The Man of Wax: Critical Essays on George Moore* (New York: New York University Press, 1971) and Graham Owens, ed., *George Moore's Mind and Art* (New York: Barnes & Noble, 1970).

3 According to Anna Gruetzner of the University of Reading, Moore's art criticism is less perceptive than his adaptations of aesthetic theories derived from painting would lead readers to expect. Professor Gruetzner's analysis of Moore's essays on art, now in progress, focuses on a significant aspect of Moore's development that to date has not received the scholarly attention it deserves.

4 'George Moore and the Nineties', in *The Man of Wax*, p. 124.

5 *George Moore: A Reconsideration*, p. xi.

6 On hearing in Paris of Moore's death, Joyce immediately instructed that a wreath bearing his name be sent in time for the funeral. Frequent references in letters of the next few days (23 January 1922, 29 January 1933, 6 February 1933) express his vexation that the newspapers did not take note of his tribute: 'I did what I thought was right in view of his age and eminence', he wrote to W.K. Magee (21 March 1933). See Stuart Gilbert, ed., *The Letters of James Joyce* (New York, 1957), pp. 333–336.

7 Introduction, *Letters to Lady Cunard*, ed. Rupert Hart-Davis (London: Rupert Hart-Davis, 1957), p. 11.

8 Cave, p. 9.

9 *PMLA* 59 (June 1944), pp. 540–55.

10 Collet, op. cit.; Ferguson, *The Influence of Flaubert on George Moore* (Philadelphia: University of Pennsylvania Press, 1934); Noel, op. cit.

11 *A Disciple of Walter Pater* (Philadelphia: University of Pennsylvania Press, 1931).

12 *George Moore's Naturalistic Prose*, Upsala Irish Studies No. 3 (Upsala: Lundequist, 1952).

13 Hough, op. cit.

14 Dunleavy, op. cit.

MOORE HALL, 1952: AN INTRODUCTION TO GEORGE MOORE ON THE 100TH ANNIVERSARY OF HIS BIRTH

RICHARD J. BYRNE

Strange as it may seem to George Moore scholars, it is still possible to go through the Irish educational system without ever hearing mention of his name. Not only that, but it is also possible to be inclined toward the study of history, literature, and art, and still sail along oblivious of the existence of his novels, short stories, and autobiographical writings, unless some enlightened soul might tell you something about him or lend you one of his books – an extremely unlikely situation, given the fact that, as Edwin Gilcher has pointed out in his essay, 'Collecting Moore', most are now rare items. Such was the case with myself thirty-one years ago, when I left secondary school with a good knowledge of literature in English (so I thought), a great ignorance of Anglo-Irish literature (which I did not recognize), and – to be fair to the Jesuits – a great love of Irish literature in the original *Gaeilge*, from which I have had many pleasurable years. And to add astonishment to surprise, I had been reared in the west of Ireland, on the edge of George Moore country, close by the hills and lakes and grassy fields that he himself had known as a boy.

At the time when I finished secondary school, although some of the teachers tried to talk to me about going on to the university, my own feeling was that I was not really given to scholarship. My father, a practical man, declared that in that case I should earn a living; he suggested that I follow his footsteps into the Electricity Supply Board. I applied and was accepted by the E.S.B., and after a few stifling months in an office, where I was taught the rudiments of map making and surveying and the use and tender care of a theodolite, I was deemed ready to take up my position in the South Mayo Rural gang.

So it was that, at the tender age of nineteen, I was deposited one fine spring day, complete with bicycle and suitcase, in the main street of the little market town of Ballinrobe, County Mayo, at the head of the Ballyglass road. The truck driver, an old friend, wished me good luck and God speed, and told me to beware of Mayo women (he was married to one himself). He also warned me that if ever I felt overcome by a sudden urge to write poetry, I should get out of there as fast as my bike would carry me – and oh, yes, that I must not forget to write home to my mother.

Well, there I stood, filled with the importance of my very first full-time job, a Map Man/Surveyor with the E.S.B. destined to cycle and walk the length and breadth of County Mayo, selecting the best positions for the electricity poles which were to carry the power into the homes of the sons and daughters and grandchildren of George Moore's tenants and neighbours. For in the early 1950s, a great portion of Ireland (and indeed England) was still without electricity, as I was still without knowledge of George Moore and his works.

I can't remember now whether we appreciated it or not at the time, but those of us who worked in those rural gangs were fortunate enough to witness, first hand, a life style that had remained virtually unchanged for hundreds of years – and which, after we had passed with our poles and wires, never would be the same again. In rural homes food still was cooked over open fires in the same great iron pots that had been used by the grandparents of those 1952 residents. Only in some of the newer houses were there turf-burning ranges. Light was provided by oil lamps and candles. When a member of the family moved about from one part of the house to the other, a candle was carried to light the way. Radios were extremely rare. Where they existed at all, they were great cumbersome monsters in mahogany or rosewood veneered cases, powered by wet-cell batteries which lasted only a few weeks at most before being carried to the nearest garage to be recharged. Needless to say, television was unknown. The people of the area were still living the same sort of lives that their fathers and grandfathers had lived, making their own amusements and pastimes. Because petrol and cars were still scarce (the second World War had ended but recently), except for special occasions, such as a visit on Saturday to the market in the nearest town or to the fair, to sell a horse or a cow, they were inclined to stay at home, or at least within the confines of the village. For personal transport the bicycle was the favoured vehicle, but for work, the horse and cart were still very much to the fore. Life proceeded at a leisurely four or five miles per hour, and all the better for it, too, as people could still talk to one another as they passed. In this way the neighbourhood news passed from mouth to mouth, and the community was the thing. It was the way in which the news of George Moore's birth, on February 24, 1852, must have reached the parents and grandparents of the men and women I met in 1952. It was the way in which they themselves – those old enough at the time, at least – must have heard of his death on January 21, 1933.

But to return to my arrival in Mayo. The road from Ballinrobe to Ballyglass is about eight miles long, and at that time it was unpaved, so with my suitcase tied to the carrier on the back of my bike I hummed along what must be one of the nicest country lanes in the west, with a small dust cloud spurting up behind me. I passed by fine, sturdy, stone farmhouses, many of them two-storied, and all of them with fine stone outbuildings which had stood for many years. All along the road were large, well-stocked fields, with high limestone walls, bespeaking comfortable circumstances; none of the forbidding craggy fields of Connemara here, where you would be hard put sometimes to find the grazing of a snipe, but good limestone land that nourished sleek cows and their offspring. There were other, poorer farms in this area, too, but I was unaware of them at the time, seeing only a pleasant green land in that fine spring sunshine. I remember that as being one of the most enjoyable bicycle rides in my career, and although I cycled that same road again many times in rain and wind, I never again felt that same feeling of well-being that I had that first day.

The village of Ballyglass is hardly a village at all, with no real main street as such, but a loose scattering of houses, a school, a shop, the guards' barracks, and, of course, the hub of all village life in Ireland, the pubs. The temporary offices of the E.S.B. were, to our great delight, situated in the spare room of one of the pubs, and the stores were in the yard, so when I arrived, I hadn't to search very hard to find my way to base. I was made to feel very welcome by everyone and taken away almost immediately to meet my new landlady, a decent woman who had spent many years as a priest's housekeeper in Boston, and who had retired to the old home place to raise chickens. To supplement her income she took in the occasional lodger such as myself.

I think it was that first evening, while being filled in on the local gossip, history, and geography, that I first heard mention of the Moores of Moore Hall – although, if my memory serves me, it was the older generations of Moore of which they spoke, particularly John, the first president of Connacht, who threw in his lot with the French in that abortive rising of '98 that ultimately cost him his life. George was almost dismissed as just a writer who had lived abroad a great deal. If they knew at the time that in other places in the world Moore Hall was known only because it had been *his* home and 1952 was marked because it was the 100th anniversary of *his* birth, they did not mention these facts at all. Maybe as I felt that here was life as it had been lived in the nineteenth century, they felt so, too. Maybe it did not seem possible to them, as later it did not seem possible to me, that George Moore belonged to the past. When they spoke of history, they turned further back, to the days when Mayo was noted for its famous racehorses, raised by such men as George Henry Moore, the writer's father; to the Famine; and to 'the Races at Castlebar', the rout of the English during the early days of the Rising of 1798, before the small band of farmers and tradesmen, led by the son of the Big House on Lough Carra, were themselves defeated.

My first duty as a map man was to familiarize myself with the area, so armed with the maps of the locality I would cycle out and investigate the countryside with a particular interest in the nature of the terrain, the number and size of the houses, and the most economical way to run the poles. Although I had the maps of the area and had studied them thoroughly, I was still completely unprepared for my first sight of Moore Hall. There was not a single person near by, or so it seemed, as I rounded the bend in the Carnacon road, crossed the Mulligar bridge and saw Lough Carra for the first time. I couldn't understand why it had such an eerie greenish light about it, and this was sufficient to make me dismount to investigate. I had never seen a lake before that was this colour, since all of the lakes where I come from had predictably dark bottoms because of the mud or the stones or the depth of water. But here was a strange luminosity that gave the impression of being lit from below by some unknown light source, and while I knew that it was simply the sunlight reflecting the white clay bottom of the lake from various depths, it had a sort of unreality about it that might have inspired a Yeats poem – and did undoubtedly inspire many of Moore's best descriptive passages. From where I stood by the water's edge, I saw for the first time Moore Hall, standing solid and square, overlooking the lake like some stern and stoney sentinel, and it wasn't until I drew closer later that I noticed that the windows were gone, as was the roof, and all that remained was an ivy-covered ruined shell.

At this time the Irish Forestry Department had embarked on a massive afforestation programme in an effort to create a viable timber bank, and to replace the original forests that had been plundered down all the years. To this end it had purchased Moore Hall and whatever remained of the Moore lands in the area and was engaged in planting trees, draining wetlands, and erecting fences. Since my business in the area was of an official nature, I decided to pay a visit, and if anybody threw officialdom at me, I had a legitimate reason for being there. I cycled up what remained of the driveway, pot-holed and stoney, until I reached the house itself.

Standing at the front door of Moore Hall for the first time and looking westward, I could see along the full length of Lough Carra with its edges softened by reeds, its dark craggy islands where men built castles and where holy men were said to have lived in solitude, and far away, the mountains of Partry and Tourmakeady, lying like some great blue giant all along the horizon. As I stood there, overwhelmed by this magnificent view, I tried to envision it as it might have been seen by a Moore on a bright, sunny morning. Apart from the fact that the Moores would have owned all that was visible before them, I must say I couldn't have asked for a better view with which to greet every morning, sunny or otherwise. I think that I knew then that this would be only the first of many visits to Moore Hall while I was in the area – and, of course, that has been the case, not only while I was stationed there, but many, many times since. The only real pity is that the Forestry Department, in its enthusiasm to plant as many trees as possible, did so on every available acre of ground, including the lawns and parklands in front of the house, and while the area is now a well-developed national park and picnic area, complete with marina, the trees have matured, most of them being pine and thirty or forty feet in height, and they now completely obliterate that wonderful view from the house out across the lake. It is still possible, of course, to look across from the water's edge, but lacking the elevation, the sheer majesty of the site as I first saw it is gone forever. Gone, too, is the chance to explore the house as I did. Its entrances are now barricaded in the interests of public safety, so curious visitors no longer can wander through the ruins and try to imagine them as they might have been in Moore's day, when he was entertaining perhaps Yeats and Martyn and Gogarty and all the rest of his literary cronies of that age. Perhaps he never did entertain them there, but it was pleasant to let my imagination run on a bit, just as one can today in, say, Coole Park, Lady Gregory's former estate, where we know they all visited, because they carved their initials on the trunk of a large copper beech there which still stands for all the world to see. The occasional surviving bits of plaster frieze in what was once drawing room or dining room of Moore Hall also served to tantalize my imagination, filling the house with ghosts, rather than constraining my mind to form only an idea of how the complete house might have appeared.

Objectively, as a house, Moore Hall was a not overly handsome Georgian structure, built, upon his return to Ireland in 1795, by the

George Moore who had traded successfully and become a wealthy merchant in Alicante. It stands square and solid on the brow of Muckloon hill, completely dominating the landscape for miles around in the grand manner of many contemporary houses – notably the very similar St. George house in Kilcolgan, Tyrone House, which now stands ruined for the same reasons and in the same manner. Moore Hall was burned to the ground on the first day of February, 1923, by a group of young men claiming to be members of the Irish Republican Army who, having advised O'Reilly, Moore's steward, to vacate the place, put it to the torch. Joseph Hone, in his *Life of George Moore* (New York: Macmillan, 1936), says that although the reason suspected at the time, by Moore himself and his friends, was that his brother Maurice was a senator (it was I.R.A. policy during the Civil War to burn the houses of senators), the real reason may have been agrarian rather than political. Whatever the truth – and I doubt it will ever be known now – it seems that there was some backlash within the I.R.A. for the burning of the house, particularly in the light of the republican nature of George Moore's great-uncle, who was held then in high esteem and still is to some extent by those with long republican memories. This report would seem to be borne out by the monument to the Moores that stands at the entrance to Kiltoom Wood and graveyard and bears this legend:

Kiltoom Burial Place of the Moores of Moorehall.
This Catholic Patriot Family is honoured for their Famine Relief and their refusal to barter principles for English Gold
Erected by Ballyglass Coy. Old I.R.A. 1964.

Not far away, on the road to Ballinafad, where George Henry Moore, George's father, went to find his wife, Mary, is a somewhat lyrical plaque on a small stone monument which reads:

Here in a little house fondly called 'The Cot'
C Coy. of Ballyglass Battalion Old I.R.A.
was formed on a moonlit night in May 1918.

While I lived in the area, the official story to which everybody seemed to subscribe was that a bunch of the 'lads' from Tourmakeady who were on the run from the Free Staters were hiding out in Moore Hall, which was unoccupied except for the steward, O'Reilly, and that they either knocked over an oil lamp by accident, or some embers from the fire fell out on the timber floor. The place was on fire before they could stop it, according to this story, and when the fire got out of hand, they were forced to flee, since they knew it would attract the attention of friend and foe alike. Whichever of these stories is the real one, I'm afraid I don't know, but I do know that both of them were in circulation when I first saw Moore Hall in 1952, and each was repeated according to the political point of view of the teller. Both points of view, incidentally, have changed little over the intervening sixty years. Since all or most of the 'lads' involved in the burning, however it happened, must now be dead, we may continue to speculate as to the real reason to our heart's content.

Although George Moore had not actually lived in Moore Hall for some time before the fire – it was the residence for a long time of his brother Maurice, Maurice's wife, and their children – he took its destruction as a great loss. It soured his love for the people of the area, leaving a sense I expect of betrayal, since his father had done so much for the local people during the famine, selling anything he could, including his beloved racehorses, in order to sustain them, and waiving rents and dues, when other landlords of the time, many of them absentee, turned out their hapless starving tenants on the road, or had them transported to Australia and America for non-payment of rents. When some thirty years later, I was speaking with some of the locals about the event, these things were remembered, and there were still some strong feelings of guilt.

Coming, as I did, from a town that was virtually surrounded by water, I felt an unusual sense of isolation in this inland (for me) area, and it wasn't long until I found myself drawn regularly the six miles or so from my digs to the water's edge at Moore Hall, just to sit and admire it, swim in it occasionally, and wallow in the sense of well-being I felt, just being there. My friends and colleagues, many of them inlanders who never saw even a river, found it difficult to understand this urge that I felt and convinced themselves that perhaps I was satisfying another primeval urge, so they set out to follow me one evening, just to check me out. When I arrived at Moore Hall that evening, I went for my usual walk through the ruins, stood at the door and admired the view, and eventually wandered down to sit by the water and read a book. I wasn't too long there, or so it seemed, when I heard the sound of somebody walking near at hand on the gravelly beach. I looked up and there stood an attractive young woman about my own age or maybe a year or two younger, and it wasn't long until she sat down beside me and we got to talking. Marie, she said her name was, and when I said that I hadn't seen her about the place before, she said that she lived for a part of the year in New York and came home to spend summers with her father in their cottage which was not far away from where we sat. We talked about our lives and families, and it wasn't long until we became quite friendly. She invited me to the house for some tea and to meet her father, and as we were walking there, whom should we meet but my colleagues, walking along and wheeling their bicycles with knowing grins all over their faces and exaggerated greetings and questions concerning my health and the lake, and I knew that no matter what I said or did, nothing would ever convince them that I hadn't been coming this way to meet Marie all along, and that I had only invented the story about the lake to cover my tracks. The following day I was the subject of much innuendo and leg pulling, but when I didn't react with more than a smile, they were convinced that they were right and the matter was soon dropped.

My new-found friend knew the area very well, and in her father's boat we rowed the length and breadth of Lough Carra, visiting the islands and the picnic places where the Moores were said to have taken their friends in bygone summers. I was shown the place on Castle Island, opposite Kiltoom Woods, where Moore's ashes were buried, and while I never had given much thought before to cremation, as it was unknown in Ireland at the time, I could feel in my heart that this was the right way for him to be laid at rest. The other Moore family grave – in the woods, at Kiltoom, near the house – seemed dank and gloomy and not a little eerie around nightfall, but here on the rocky stone of the island, under a summer sky, a man could wait out eternity in peace.

Incidentally, for those who have not been to Moore Hall, the family burial place stands atop a little hill in the Kiltoom Woods, woods that are mostly beech, ash, sycamore, and pine, none of the trees apparently more than about a hundred years old. The grave itself is about twenty feet square, and within a small iron wicket gate and a large horizontal-type tomb. In the centre of the stone is engraved:

FORTIS CADERE CEDERE NON POTEST
GEORGE MOORE OF MOOREHALL
B. 1770 D. 1840
HIS WIFE LOUISA D. OF HON JOHN BROWNE D. 1849
AND THEIR SONS JOHN B. 1812 D. 1829
AUGUSTUS B. 1817 D. 22 MARCH 1849
GEORGE HENRY MOORE M. P. O. L
B. 1810 D. 1870
HIS WIFE
MARY D. OF MAURICE BLAKE BALLINAFAD
B. 1832 D. 1895

THEIR SON
COL. MAURICE GEORGE MOORE C. B.
B. 1854 D. 1939
LATE 1ST BATT. CONNAUGHT RANGERS
R.I.P.

Nearby is a smaller grave which, as if to give lie to the other, proclaims:

THIS STONE MARKS THE GRAVE OF
SEN. COL. MAURICE MOORE C. B.

I remember being greatly interested in this Moore when first I saw his grave, because he had been in the Connaught Rangers. My own grandfather had served in the same battalion as company sergeant major and warrant officer, in all the same points as Maurice Moore, and I fantasized that they would have known each other. What a coincidence it seemed to me that I was there; into my mind came all the imaginative things that a young man's mind conjures up.

Not far from Moore Hall, on the opposite shore – the Ballinrobe shore – I was fishing one day with Marie's father. We stopped to make the tea on the shore. While gathering driftwood to build a fire I made a discovery that gave me quite a start at the time: a lone hawthorn tree stood by the water's edge, and all over it was festooned with the bleached skulls of pike that had been caught, beheaded, and left for the carrion crows to pick clean. Apparently it was a local custom when one caught a decent size pike, but the effect was surreal, like something out of a nightmare, with forty or fifty eyeless skulls grinning and bobbing in the breeze. I wondered if George Moore had known about it or had used the custom in one of his books. I have tried many times since then to find this tree, with its strange fruit, but whether I have lost my sense of direction or whether it has gone or the skulls have just disintegrated, I don't know. But the memory of that first vision and the start it gave me are etched forever on my memory.

We fished quite a lot that summer and caught both trout and pike. But since that time, the Inland Fisheries Trust in its wisdom decided that the pike were exterminating all of the trout and embarked on a sort of pike pogrom. The result of this action seems to have been the upsetting of the natural balance of the lake, and now one cannot catch a decent pike or trout, the former having been netted, trapped, poisoned, and shot to the brink of extinction, and the latter, no longer in fear of their natural predators, having grown big and lazy and content to feed on the bottom, ignoring fishermen and flies alike. I suppose they know what they're doing at the Inland Fisheries; modern science is wonderful.

Night-time in Ballyglass and Moore Hall and the surrounding district was full of fine experiences that summer. A colleague of mine, Dennis, was a fine tenor, and I was a passable baritone. Between us we knew maybe a couple of dozen old songs or ballads. In those days, before the resurgence of interest in folk music, these songs were known as 'Comeallyes', because many of them began with a line something like 'come all ye gallant heroes and listen to my song'. . . . Hardly a night went by that there wasn't a wake or a wedding or an American wake in some house in the area, and Denny and I would be invited along as part of the entertainment. An American wake was an evening when all the neighbours and friends would gather into a house to wish God Speed to some member of the family who was going to America and to comfort those staying behind. Before Dennis and I went off for an evening, we'd make an agreement as to who would sing what song. There would be barrels of porter, a case of whiskey, a few cases of beer, a gallon or two of poteen, and spare ribs, bacon, and roast chickens to cater for the thirst and the hunger. The host family would hire in a musician, usually a ten-key melodeon player or an accordion player, and the centre of the kitchen would be cleared for dancing, while the drink and food would be laid out 'below' in the room. I remember a particular night at an American wake in Carnacon when the melodeon player had so much to drink that he fell asleep. This did not affect his performance, however, and he continued to play all of the changes for a set which was in full swing, with his head to one side, his collar open, his cap askew, and him snoring loudly. I couldn't believe his performance, but the locals who knew him said that he played better when he was asleep.

In those days, going to America was still a bit of an adventure, and it was more common for people to take the liner than to fly. So it was possible (or so it seemed) that many of those who went off across the ocean wouldn't come home again for years and years. Of course, when they did come home, there was a party for their arrival as well, so there was always fierce excitement in the neighbourhood when somebody had a 'Yank' coming home. Everybody knew that there would be at least one party if not two in that house. How many new Untilled Fields George Moore might have written had he been with us in Mayo that summer!

About two miles north of Moore Hall stands the ruins of Clogher House, similar in many ways to the ruins of Moore Hall, but one which in my time was still occupied by the late James Fitzgerald Kenny, who held the position of Minister in the first Irish government after the Treaty (1921). I remember him as a small, dignified white-haired man who was astounded at the proposed cost of installing electricity in his large house. The system of laying a fixed charge for electricity was related exactly to the size of the house, and in his case it was enormous. Some years later, I was involved in the National Gaelic Theatre – the *Taibhdhearc* – and was party to buying this old man's entire travelling wardrobe of elegant clothes and his sister's clothes as well for the wardrobes department of the theatre. Many of the articles of clothing are still strutting their hour on the *Taibhdhearc* stage. No doubt they are the kinds of clothes the Moores would have worn, too. I only wish I had talked with the old man about the Moores instead of the electricity rates, so that his stories might still be serving our imaginations, too.

A rather grim and macabre tale I recall being told concerned a tree that stood near the entrance to this house. It must have been a story known to Moore; I'm surprised that he did not use it in one of his books. The tree was a high blasted tree upon which nothing grew, and it was said that it died when a local man, accused of being an informer for the police or the Black and Tans, was hanged there naked one night, following a local kangaroo court. It was known by the neighbours who perpetrated the murder, and they say a curse was put on the men responsible and on their families forever. Whether this was true or not I cannot say, but my informant assured me that the year hadn't gone by but all three of the men involved had met with horrible accidents and been killed or crippled or maimed or all three together, and not only that, but their children had been born retarded and deformed. I never checked out the story, but the tree certainly had an ominous look about it, and I was assured that the story was true. Both the tree and the gateway are since gone.

Near Clogher, in Carrownacon or Carnacon Churchyard (both spellings are used), is the empty grave in which John Moore lay until he was exhumed and reinterred with great honours on the Mall in Castlebar, some hundred and fifty years after he became a hero for his part in the Races of Castlebar. His twentieth-century burial site has been attracting attention since publication of *The Year of the French* by Thomas Flanagan, a historical novel that deals blow by blow with the abortive rising, and with the way in which the Irish led by John Moore and the French led by General Humbert fought side by side. It has also attracted visitors to Moore Hall, which is featured in the novel. Although Flanagan exercises the novelist's prerogative and makes the headstrong John the younger brother, the practical George the older (the sons of the merchant from Alicante were actually, in order of birth, Peter, who apparently was retarded, John, who was indeed both headstrong and handsome, and George, the novelist's grandfather), he seems to have portrayed their characters accurately. Visitors cannot enter the house, of course, but on one of the centre pillars of the entrance they can read a plaque placed there by George Moore's nephew, on the occasion of the reburial of John Moore. It reads:

MOORE HALL 1792–1923
IN MEMORY OF JOHN MOORE
FIRST PRESIDENT OF IRELAND, AND
THE MEN OF THIS PARISH WHO GAVE THEIR
LIVES FOR IRELAND IN THE RISING OF 1798
ERECTED BY MAURICE C. MOORE
    CALIF. U.S.A.

Probably the best-known architectural attraction of the area near Moore Hall is Ballintubber Abbey, three to four miles to the north. Built in 1216 on the site of a fifth-century patrician church and unroofed (although in regular use) for hundreds of years, the Abbey was finally restored, after a long history of periodic but incomplete destruction followed by a long history of attempted renovation, in 1966. In 1952, much of the restoration work was still to be done, and the Abbey looked much as it did in Moore's time – and as he describes it in many of his writings. I remember it as an impressive, awe-inspiring edifice enhanced by its history. Founded by Cathal O Conor of the Wine Red Hand, King of Ireland, in appreciation for the kindness of an O Sheridan who had sheltered Cathal and his mother when they were fleeing from their enemies, it was first planned as a substitute for the older, crumbling church. Through some error, however, the order for the construction was misunderstood, and a new church was built not where O Sheridan had requested it in Ballintubber (Phadraig) – The Town of Patrick's Well, in County Mayo – but in Ballintubber (Bhrighde), The Town of Bridget's Well, in County Roscommon. When the mistake was discovered, Cathal vowed to rectify it by building a church 'seven times more magnificent' on the proper site.

During most of George Moore's early life in Mayo the Abbey would have appeared as it is shown in 1865 photographs in *The Story of Ballintubber Abbey* by the Rev. Thomas Egan, who supervised completion of the restoration project in 1966. While Moore was growing up, the Abbey was part of the Moore estate: in

1795 his great-grandfather had purchased the Abbey lands from the
Blakes of Galway, who in turn had obtained them in 1603 when
James I had given instructions that they be disposed of. Of the many
stories about the Abbey, one – surviving only in a doggerel verse
that my grandfather used to recite, to entertain me, when I was a
child – involves John Moore:

> Shake hands brother John
> You're a rogue and I'm another
> You'll be hung in Ballinrobe
> And I'll be hung in Ballintubber.

I have never been able to determine what it means. Other stories of
the Abbey are more complete. One tells of the death of Tioboid na
Long (Theobold of the Ships), also known as Sir Thebold, son of the
famous Elizabethan pirate queen, Grania Uaile (Grace O'Malley),
by her second husband, Richard in Iron de Burgo. Having inherited
his mother's fleet and her prowess on the high seas, Tioboid had
supported the crown forces against the Spaniards when they landed
at Kinsale; in recognition of this service, Charles I had created him
the first Viscount Mayo in 1627. Killed outside the Abbey by his
brother-in-law, Diarmeen O'Conor of Sligo, who was of a different
political persuasion, Tioboid was buried in the de Burgo Chapel
(now the Sacristy) where his altar-like tomb with its inscription,
'Tioboid na Long, 1st Viscount Lord Mayo', may still be seen. In
1653 Cromwell's soldiers attacked and attempted to burn the
Abbey, but much of its sturdy stone structure survived.

Ruins of castles on the islands of Lough Carra also fascinated
Moore and found their way into his writings, as Gareth W.
Dunleavy tells us in his essay, 'Moore's Medievalism: A Modern
Triptych.' And as Janet E. Dunleavy explains in *George Moore: The
Artist's Vision, the Storyteller's Art* (Lewisburg, Pa.: Bucknell
University Press, 1973), Moore Hall itself provides the interior of
Woodview, the home of the Barfields, where Esther Waters works
as a housemaid. (George Moore gives Woodview's location as near
Shoreham, in Sussex, to justify calling his novel 'An English Story',
no doubt, but I have heard from local people that Esther was really
Irish.) The plaster frieze of the Moore Hall drawing room and
dining room, fragments of which I saw in 1952, was used by Moore
in his description of the home of Lucy Bentham of *A Modern Lover*.
Book in hand, readers of *The Lake* and *A Storyteller's Holiday* can
still become almost as familiar today with the district around Moore
Hall as I was in 1952.

Since 1952, although many times I have returned to Moore Hall, time and fortune have not always allowed me to be there as often as I have wished. But I now know what I never learned in secondary school: that house, hill, and lake are available to me in the pages of George Moore's books – when I can find a bookseller with the odd copy he is willing to part with. There's no doubt the old bicycle was cheaper.

GEORGE MOORE'S PARIS

JANE CRISLER

The years George Moore lived in Paris – 1873 to 1880 – are years of muddled transition in the political and social life of France. The 1870s had had a dramatic beginning, marked by military defeat, loss of territory, political collapse of the Second Empire, and urban revolution in the Paris Commune. These tumultuous events were followed by an all-pervasive desire for peace. The national government, a republic, emerged by default; the National Assembly, comprised of a majority of monarchists, was housed at Versailles. Although the Empire had ended, monarchist rule had not disappeared from French consciousness. It was understood that a king would ascend to the throne, but no one knew who it would be. The Bourbon Comte de Chambord was the legitimate pretender, but the conditions he demanded, essentially a complete restoration of the *ancien régime* of the eighteenth century, were unacceptable. His acknowledged successors from the more liberal House of Orléans awaited their turn while supporters of both royal lines intrigued. Rivalries eventually undermined the royalist cause, strengthening the republic. In 1873, however, the year in which George Moore arrived to study art, an interim solution to the problem of ascension was reached with the election of Marshal MacMahon to the role of caretaker president. His term lasted until 1880, the year George Moore returned to Ireland; it bought time for royal negotiations and for assuring the nation's peace. During this period, the monarchist republic was dominated by a restoration mentality that placed a high value on moral order. Repressive measures enacted under imperial rule continued: they controlled the press, the theatres, and the right of association and other civil liberties. The Legitimists, supporters of the reactionary Chambord, added another dimension to government conservativism: religion. MacMahon's monarchist minister, the Duc de Broglie, instituted what became known as the '*Ordre moral*', which was described in the President's opening speech to the National Assembly in 1873. The government supported national pilgrimages and other forms of traditional religious practice; *non-pratiquants*, those who did not participate in traditional Catholic rituals, were considered subversive opponents of the state. Most visible of the new regime's commitments to restoring order through the Catholic Church was the National Assembly's expropriation of the site at Montmartre where the Archbishop of Paris wished to build the Basilica of Sacré-Coeur. The highest point in Paris and the scene of bloody battles during the Commune, Montmartre was preferred as a location 'so that the new church, consecrated to the Sacred Heart, would be seen to exercize a symbolic supervision of the sinful city stretched beneath it'.[1]

When he arrived in Paris, George Moore could regard a panorama from the butte of Montmartre to the Louvre on the bank of the Seine below that exemplified the ambiguities of Paris in the 1870s. The Montmartre quarter had only recently become a part of the city; it had been annexed in 1860 as part of the heroic rebuilding of Paris undertaken by Emperor Napoleon III and executed by the Prefect of the Seine, Baron Georges Haussmann.[2] Their programme had transformed Paris from an unsanitary agglomeration of medieval slums into the most modern city in Europe. They had altered the topography of the city, opening up once dark and crowded neighbourhoods with vast boulevards, bordered by buildings of classic uniformity and planted with trees. In his plans for Paris Napoleon III aspired to the magnificence of Rome and the verdant delicacy of Hyde Park. He rebuilt streets, adding ninety miles of thoroughfares, and embellished the city with rustic parks. His first great project was the Bois de Boulogne on the western outskirts of the city. He then rebuilt the Bois de Vincennes to balance the plan on the east side. The two grand parks, with their artificial lakes, riding paths, and entertainments, lie on an east-west axis that traverses the city. At the centre of this line is the Louvre, which had first been a fortress, then the home of French kings, the last residents being Napoleon III and Empress Eugenie. To the north of the Louvre is the 'Right Bank', where now aristocratic residences, Second Empire apartment houses, and commercial buildings extend like a fan. It encircles the historic heart of Paris. Ironically, it was the centre of the city, the collective product of a long line of ambitious monarchs, that bore the cruel scars of civil insurrection. The urban violence of the Paris Commune of 1871 had been a shocking incident in French history: workers who formed a communist government had taken over the city from the republican government housed in Versailles; over 20,000 citizens had died as the national government fought to regain control. The bloody street battles had pitted the French people against each other with a

bitterness and futility that had not been seen before. Communards disillusioned with national government in any form burned the Tuileries Palace, which had formed the western boundary of the desmesne of the Louvre, and the Hotel de Ville, seat of the municipal administration. If the post-war atmosphere of the city was calm, it was partly because there was a national desire for peace, partly as a result of exhaustion and paranoia. By 1873 the radical voices of the Commune had been exiled; they would not be heard again in France until the general amnesty of 1880.

The Paris that George Moore saw for the first time when, a young man of twenty-one, he arrived at the Gare du Nord on the north-east side of the French capital, was a city of paradox, governed by an absent regime with an empty throne. Within the city various social groups – *ancien régime* aristocrats, *nouveaux arrivés* of the Second Empire, the working classes, and the growing bourgeoisie – coexisted and struggled to maintain their position. Each of these groups was a closed world unto itself, in which family and professional life were carefully circumscribed and protected.[3] Yet new forms of sociability had developed since the Revolution of 1789 which allowed outsiders to meet interesting people at every level of the social ladder. As a foreigner with money to spend, Moore was able to circulate within the margins of these different constituencies. Though he prided himself on his acculturation to French life, his early experiences were clearly those fashioned for foreigners in a city disposed to tourism.

In his peregrinations about Paris, George Moore unwittingly followed a map that traced French cultural development from the preceding century to the 1870s and that governed, in some respects, the outline of his own aesthetic evolution. He was introduced to the French capital in the quiet of early morning; he saw a 'great gray and melancholy' station surrounded by the 'miserable carriages' of a 'tall, haggard city'. His impression was of 'pale, sloppy, yellow houses; an oppressive absence of colour; a peculiar bleakness in the streets'.[4] Moore's impression was shared by another voyager, coming from the opposite direction, from Italy, who found the unanimated city equally devoid of character, 'still sleepy and disheveled', early in the morning. 'How ugly Paris is at that hour!' he declared. 'Those famous boulevards, so bright and gleaming, but a short time since, are only great irregular streets lined with miserable houses, high and low, faded, tarnished and crowned on the summits with a horrible confusion of tall chimneys which seem like the frame-work of unfinished buildings; and everything being still closed and veiled, one only sees a gray and solitary space'.[5]

Moore's first stop, a hotel with an English-speaking proprietress, was located on the Quai Voltaire, across the Seine from the Louvre, in one of the oldest neighbourhoods in the city. The Latin Quarter had traditionally attracted scholars and students from all over the world; it was the site of important religious establishments during the Middle Ages. Though the rebuilding of Paris under Napoleon III had left standing many of the medieval landmarks of the Left Bank, slum clearance and modernization had eliminated many of its more picturesque streets. Broad thoroughfares such as the new Boulevard St. Michel cut a wide swath through crowded quarters, virtually obliterating the old Paris described by Balzac (Hemmings, p. 131). The École des Beaux-Arts where Moore studied met in a conglomeration of historical buildings. The oldest portion of the complex housed architectural fragments from the old Church of St. Genevieve, dating from the eleventh century; a fountain from the twelfth century; and numerous other medieval artifacts. The main building of the École occupied the site of the Couvent des Petits Augusts, founded by Marguerite de Valois, Henri IV's eccentric first wife whom he later divorced. Nineteenth-century tourists visiting the École were entertained with a variety of legends associated with the Queen's oeuvre and its history.

When soon after his arrival in Paris Moore moved from the Left Bank to the Boulevard des Italiens, he made an intuitive migration from the world of rarified abstraction to one of immediate materialism. The pleasures of the Left Bank – book-stalls lining the quays, landmark buildings with ancient histories, and academic instruction conducted in accordance with classical formulas – had to be mined to be appreciated. The Right Bank was the temporal world. In Moore's words, it was 'what a toy shop had been fifteen years before: everything was spick and span, and every illusion was set out straight and smart in new paint and gilding' (*Confessions*, p. 57). He set himself right in the middle of the social whirl. The Hôtel de Russie, situated on the Rue Drouot facing the Boulevard des Italiens, was located in one of the most congested areas of Paris. This was the *boulevardier*'s Paris to which Moore had aspired when he stepped off the train in the Gare du Nord. 'Here is the burning heart of Paris, the high road to mundane triumphs, the great theatre of the ambitions and of the famous dissolutenesses, which draws to itself the gold, vice and folly of the four quarters of the globe' (De Amicis, p. 10). This section of Paris had not suffered physical devastation during either the Franco-Prussian War or the Commune. All of the riches of Paris were there for Moore to see, the door to his toy shop was wide open:

Here is splendour at its height; this is the metropolis of metropolises, the open and lasting palace of Paris, to which all aspire and everything tends. Here the street becomes a square, the sidewalk a street, the shop a museum, the café a theatre, beauty elegance, splendour dazzling magnificence, and life a fever. The horses pass in troops, and the crowd in torrents. Windows, signs, advertisements, doors, facades, all rise, widen and become silvered, gilded and illumined. It is a rivalry of magnificence and stateliness which borders on madness' (De Amicis, p. 10).

With this move, Moore had entered the world of 'the boulevards', a series of broad avenues which stretch in a semi-circle from the elegant church of the Madeleine to the Place de la Bastille, tracing the city's seventeenth-century boundaries. Already the fashionable place to be seen during the *ancien régime*, the boulevards became even more popular after the Revolution of 1789. With the further cultivation of outdoor recreation under Napoleon III, the open air and public event replaced the salon and private space as the place to meet people and be seen.

The geography of Paris is much the same today as when Moore strolled the famous boulevards. The Boulevard des Italiens is still the keystone of the arch of open space lying to the north of the Seine river. To the west it joins the Boulevard des Capuchines, which intersects the Place de l'Opéra where, in Moore's time, the new Opera House, commissioned by Napoleon III and extravagantly designed by Garnier, was the site of many public balls after its grand opening in 1875. The Boulevard de la Madeleine extends west from the Place de l'Opéra to terminate in front of the classic church. From the Madeleine, the Rue Royale runs south into the Place de la Concorde, the broad plaza between the Tuileries gardens and the Champs-Elysées. This was, then as now, the more elegant section of *'les boulevards'*. As the nineteenth century closed, the Champs-Elysées became the most popular avenue for promenades. New commercial enterprizes and fashionable residential buildings developed in neighbourhoods to the north. The aristocratic remnants of the *ancien régime* and Second Empire settled in these environs, recreating the elegant salons, dinner parties, and entertainments of former times. The Hôtel de Russie, where Moore resided, was located at the juncture of the Boulevard des Italiens and the Boulevard Montmartre. From its side windows, Moore would have seen the Rue Drouot to the north of the boulevards. Just one block from the Hôtel de Russie, in fact, was the Hôtel des Ventes Drouot, the Paris 'Christie's' where Moore and his fellow studio artists ridiculed the early Impressionist exhibitions. South of the boulevards, the Rue Drouot becomes the Rue de Richelieu,

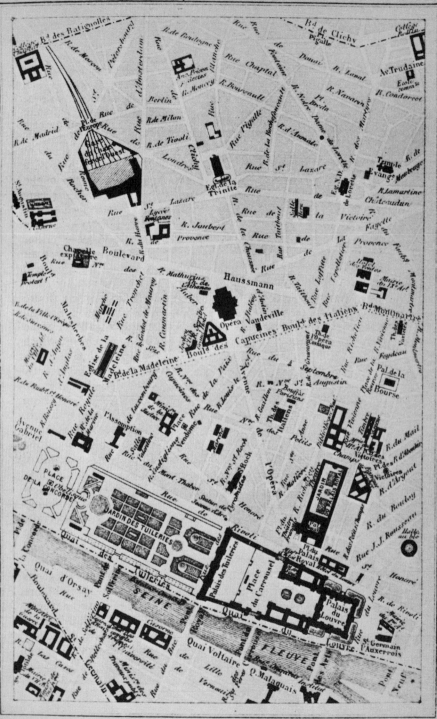

which runs in a straight line past the Bibliothèque Nationale and the Palais Royal to the Louvre. The Rue Vivienne, parallel to the Rue de Richelieu, formed the western boundary of the block housing Jullian's studio, where Moore strove to become an artist. Also in that block, on the north side facing the Boulevard Montmartre, was the Théâtre des Variétés, one of the many theatres in the quarter where contemporary and popular dramas were staged. Seven more boulevards, including the Boulevard Poissonière, complete the system which ends at the Place de la Bastille. As in London, the eastern section of this area is less glamorous than its western counterpart: it traverses less wealthy neighbourhoods populated primarily by artisans who produce many of the luxury goods sold in fine shops. At the time of Moore's Parisian sojourn many of the bronze works displayed on the shelves of shops in the Rue Vivienne, Palais-Royal, and the Chausée-d'Antin were produced by workers living in the seventeenth- and eighteenth-century houses in this quarter. To the east of this section of the boulevards and the Place de la Bastille is the working class suburb of Saint Antoine. Labourers occupying this quarter traditionally have been republican. These are the people who rushed to storm the fortress of the Bastille in 1789 and who transformed the Boulevard de Beaumarchais to the north of the Bastille into a major theatre of the 1848 Revolution. In Moore's time and still today, the popular forms of entertainment offered in the circus, the cabarets, and theatres are the major attraction of the eastern leg of the boulevards.

The open, public quality of boulevard life permitted a mingling of classes and styles which never would have been possible in private salons. A popular guidebook, sold in Paris during the 1870s, describes the special quality of the city's boulevards:

Paris, la ville de l'égalité, la ville démocratique par excellence, a voulu avoir dans son enceinte une promenade qui représentât, qui servit les besoins de la foule, et qui appartînt à tous ... il créa avec amour la véritable promenade de l'avenir, le véritable jardin de la nation émancipée, les Boulevards.[7]

However, although Paris was the 'city of equality', the aristocracy set fashions, and conspicuous consumption was a major pastime. The industrialization and free-trade policies of the Second Empire promoted the development of both large department stores and specialized shops selling luxury goods. Fashion became accessible to the middle classes. The worlds of aesthetics and consumerism merged, resulting – in the eyes of many observers – in the trivialization of art (Hemmings, p. 150 et passim).

The boulevard seems like one immeasurable hall of an enormous museum, where the gold, gems, laces, flowers, crystals, bronzes, pictures, all the masterpieces of industry, all the seductions of art, all the finery of riches, and all the caprices of fashion are crowded together and displayed in a profusion which startles, and a grace which enamours (De Amicis, pp. 10–11).

In the boulevard shops was the pastiche which so offended the aesthetic critics of the Second Empire. The bronze works of Paris's traditional artisan studios were displayed next to antiques and avant-garde paintings. During the 1870s Impressionist painters penetrated these galleries, offering their new style of art for sale. Ironically, although the spontaneity of their representation captured the frenetic atmosphere of the boulevard, it offended the conservative taste of the *boulevardier*. When Edward Dayne and his friend Marshall of *Confessions* hoped to earn money by selling their paintings, they produced conventional studio compositions. The fate of Marshall, painting porcelain for sale in the boulevard shops, was probably common among the city's aspiring artists. The profusion of retail establishments, cafés, and restaurants along the boulevard engendered a new social type, the *flâneur*, a person who had perfected the art of window-shopping and social observation. To be a competent *flâneur*, one had to have both time to devote to seemingly aimless wanderings up and down the boulevards and the sensibility to appreciate the spectacle. A *flâneur* is a self-conscious observer – he appreciates what he sees and intends that others should see him with the same esteem.

A *flâneur par excellence*, especially after he had passed through his 'dandy' phase of fine clothes and manners, Moore had ample opportunity when roaming the boulevards to select the painter whom he wanted to emulate. After he eventually made his choice, a studio of artists was available to him within a short distance up a quiet side street from the boulevard. Behind the uniform façades of the buildings lining the grand boulevards were honeycombs of shops, studios, and lodgings, known as *passages* if they opened onto a street and *galeries* if they ended in a cul-de-sac. The open space between parallel buildings was covered with glass, creating a small city, a precursor of contemporary shopping centers and planned communities.

The Passage des Panoramas, where Moore attended studio classes and later lived, is located south of the Boulevard Montmartre, just two blocks to the east of the Hôtel de Russie. Built in the early nineteenth century, utilizing the innovative technologies of iron and glass, it owes its name to a series of panoramas representing Paris, Lyons, London, and Naples which were installed by Robert Fulton, the inventor of the steam engine. The money which he made by exhibiting the panoramas enabled him to continue his experiments in marine locomotion.[8] An English journalist, George Sala, fascinated by the display of 'an ever-moving, ever-interesting picture of human life', described the Passage at length.[9] He traced his way through the labyrinth, beginning with 'a noted sweet-stuff shop, in which I should say that it would be practicable for a young gentleman with plenty of ready money and a generous disposition to ruin himself at New Year and Paschal tides with the utmost promptitude and despatch'. He faced considerable temptation in the bookbinder's shop located further down the passage, where 'Everything that can be done in the shape of embossed, indented, and inlaid moroco, russian, roan, vellum, and calf – of emblazoned backs and tooled edges – seems to have been lavished on the embellishment of rare editions' (Sala, p. 76). Continuing through the passage, Sala moved from the main gallery to its ancillary branches:

Straying from the main avenue, full as it is of jewellers, confectioners, fancy stationers, toyshops, and dealers in old Dresden and new Sèvres, you stray up 'all manner of streets' – or passages – as Leigh Hunt's pig did. One gallery takes you into another, and so, you know not how, you struggle into the Rue Vivienne. Another corridor gives me egress into a narrow purblind street, where my barber resides. He is a little round puncheon of a man, with head of bushy black hair, and sparkling black eyes – a Provençal from Marseilles' (p. 78).

This character, so similar to Moore's Julien of *Confessions*, stands in contrast to the ritualized world of the boulevard: 'At all events the barber and his family, together with a few beggars whom I have held brief converse with, are the most natural folk that I have met with during my sojourn in Paris' (Sala, p. 78). The Passage housed restaurants offering sustenance at more reasonable prices than the boulevards. 'In one of the Passages I find a restaurant – a fixed price one. Breakfast, two francs fifty; dinners, three francs, I think' (Sala, p. 78). More substantial fare was available at the Ristorante del Matto Forestiere where 'you will find Italian cookery of a better kind than you can hope to meet with in Italy itself at the present day', and at 'phenomenally cheap' prices. Like the character of the barber's family, the ambience of the restaurant contrasted sharply with that of the boulevard: 'the place is characteristic and genuine; and that is something to find in the midst of a wilderness of French eating-houses, where conventionality has come to the complexion of the most wearisome monotony' (Sala, p. 79).

Qualities of the passage that Sala found entertaining and quaint could be oppressive to others. The latter half of the century was a period of rapid industrialization and urbanization for France. The covered passageways provided a sheltered arcade for shopping at the lower levels, but in its more remote sections and at higher levels, where cheap apartments could be found, the atmosphere was confining. Moore noted that 'it was not pleasant that your window should open, not to the sky, but to an unclean prospect of glass roofing' (*Confessions*, p. 71). Julien's frequent excursions to Meudon outside the city fortifications on the southwest side must have been both a Mediterranean custom and a response to his need for recreation in the open air. The presence of these two Mediterranean characters in the *démodé* interior of the Passage – Sala's barber, Moore's Julien – suggests a greater community of immigrants in the vicinity of the boulevards. Provincial peasants poured into Paris to work in the factories and service occupations of the city. The area north of the boulevards was populated primarily by working class people, immigrants from the provinces of France or from other countries. They tended to settle in the Montmartre quarter, as they continue to do today, due to the availability of cheap housing. As Moore learned the French language and became acquainted with the people of Paris, he was able to meet many of the artists and writers who shuttled between the quaint authenticity of the poor Montmartre district and the glitter of the grand boulevards.

Although Napoleon III had incorporated Montmartre into the city, he did not have a chance to modernize this quarter as he did other areas of the city. It retained its unique character with one imperial improvement: the limestone quarries were closed. The southern side of the mount was the most modern; the streets and houses constructed there since the 1840s resembled those of Paris. To the west, the mount had remained unchanged from the eighteenth century. The narrow, winding streets and houses out of another century suggested that the quarter was really an old provincial town, lost in the interior of France. In 1870 the quarter contained many country houses, surrounded by gardens, which could be reached only by a solitary road. More than any other section of Paris it reminded rural immigrants of their *pays*. In Moore's time, it attracted artists and writers who had been dispossessed from their bohemian haunts by the Emperor's modernization plan. The local population, composed mainly of cabaret and restaurant owners and wage-earners, were hospitable and colourful. The elevation of the butte made it an excellent site for windmills. These functional structures gave their names to local cabarets which were to develop into famous night spots in later decades. Two of the most renown were the Moulin de la Galette and the Moulin Debray. On the south and east sides of the mount were gardens, such as the Château-Rouge, a favourite of Edward Dayne and Marshall, where public balls were held. The closing of the quarries had chased the vagabonds and thieves from the quarter, making it safe for people from all over Paris to enjoy Montmartre's entertainments. Every evening its inexpensive prices and charming atmosphere attracted armies of wage-earners, women of dubious attraction, and impoverished landholders (*Paris Illustré*, pp. 287–288). This last category was comprised of men a little less comfortable financially than Moore. Many a young man who had come to find his fortune in the City of Lights and had exhausted his allowance from home found diversion in the streets of Montmartre. Here, the margins of different social worlds intersected, introducing respectable bourgeois gentlemen to women of the *demi-monde*, offering raucous entertainment and a chance for self-expression outside of established society.

Beneath the steps of Sacré-Coeur, another band of boulevards encircles the city, an almost concentric ring north of the grand boulevards where Moore lived. During the latter 1870s, Moore spent much of his time in the vicinity of the Boulevard de Clichy, which originates at the Place de Clichy in the west, meanders northeast for two blocks, then turns east and runs through the Place Pigalle. Between the two rings of boulevards were residential neighbourhoods of Montmartre, criss-crossed by modest streets. Here were the homes, studios, and cafés frequented by the habitués of the Nouvelles Athènes. The charming neighbourhoods of the Rue de Douai, Rue Condorcet, Rue de la Rouchefoucauld, and the street where Moore lived, the Rue de la Tour des Dames, lay to the south and southeast of the Place de la Pigalle. To the west around the Place de l'Europe just north of the Gare St. Lazare was the developing quarter fashionable among the middle classes: Manet's neighbourhood. The Rue de St. Pétersbourg (now Rue de Léningrad), where Manet's parents lived and where he had a studio, runs south from the Place de Clichy into the Place de l'Europe. Also fanning out from the Place de Clichy are the Rue d'Amsterdam and the Rue de Clichy. Ten or fifteen minutes suffice for a pedestrian to walk from elegant promenades to the apex of the butte of Montmartre. In this respect, Paris offered Moore a social environment similar to that which he would have known in Dublin: within a few blocks compact and dense with human experience and possibilities, he was able to leave the ritualized pageantry of *'les boulevards'* and enter the archaic and anachronistic world of Montmartre's cafés.

The café occupies a very special place in French political and cultural history. As the name suggests, it was at first an establishment in which coffee, a novelty when the drink was first introduced to Europe, was served to the public. The concept of sophistication associated with the proferred refreshment carried over to the institution itself, with individual cafés becoming famous in their own right. When Moore first arrived in Paris, he headed straight toward the most renowned tourist spots on the Boulevard des Italiens. Here were the elegant establishments of the Tortoni, famous for its ice cream; the Helder; and the Maison Dorée, which served food as well. These grand cafés were places in which to be seen and to engage in social gossip. Cafés in other quarters likewise provided a forum for the activities of local residents. The café was especially important to people of lesser means who could not entertain in their homes and to individuals who had no social ties in the city. Impoverished painters, such as Monet, unmarried men like Moore living in single rooms, could all go to the café. It was a place similar to the Dublin and London public house, where people could meet, either intentionally or by chance, to discuss ideas. With the rights of association seriously curtailed in the nineteenth century (organized groups were regarded as subversive and a threat to the French state), the café offered a place for people to communicate. Proprietors came to know their habitual clients, with whom they would maintain an on-going conversation and for whom they would reserve table space and pass on news. Cafés also served as public reading rooms, offering copies of newspapers and other publications for the client to peruse. Moore was accurate in describing the café as a university, for the arts of rhetoric and criticism were actively cultivated within its boundaries.

As a social institution of significance in Moore's Paris, the café was a paradox. It offered the shelter of circumscribed space, more intimate when closed in the winter, more comfortable when open in mild weather. Yet, no matter how quaint or personal its character, it remained a public place. Here, one could come and go at will and be freer in expressing opinions or ideas than might ever be dreamed possible as a guest in a private home. Traditionally, the home has been the private domain of the French into which outsiders are not admitted. The café was a middle ground, providing a place for a man as private and as opinionated as Degas to meet and converse with Moore, a collector of gossip and opinions for whom he felt no great sympathy. Manet used his studio on the Rue de Clichy as a sort of café. It was more public than his home, where he had structured evening receptions, but more personal than the commercial café. So numerous and frequent were the visitors to his studio that his wife described it as 'an annex of the Café de Bade'.[10] For Manet, ostracized by the official art world and desirous of a friendly social life, his studio offered the perfect place. It was also a private space, separate from the home, into which the artist could invite his mistress. Here was the demi-monde where the respectable, bourgeois husband could meet the women of questionable virtue.

In 1873 the Nouvelle Athènes café, centrally located on the Place Pigalle, became the meeting place of painters, their friends, writers, and critics living in the rustic Montmartre area. Although the café no longer stands, its atmosphere was captured by Degas in his painting 'L'Absinthe' (1877) and by Manet in 'The Plum' (1877). Both paintings reveal the artists' fascination with the urban environment, with the interior of the café, and with the dissipated women of the lower classes. The proprietor regularly reserved two marble-topped tables next to the door so that his regular clientele might enjoy the coming and going of his patrons. Founders of these groups were the painters Manet, Monet, Renoir, Pissaro, Fantin-Latour, and Degas. They were joined by the writers Zandomeneghi, Rafaelli, Forain, Marcellin Desboutins, Duranty, Villiers de l'Isle-Adam, Burty, Armand Sylvestre and the *nouveau venu*, George Moore. Moore arrived on the scene around 1877 after having been introduced to Manet by Villiers de l'Isle-Adam.[11]

The background to Moore's introduction to the habitués of the Nouvelles Athènes was French society itself. In a state of discreet flux during the 1870s, it had been moving gradually from the constraints of the Restoration and Empire towards the forms of an industrialized republic. The somber tones of moral order which hung over the decade's beginning were lifting gradually; in the 1880s they gave way to a lavish flowering of the arts and a genteel way of life known as the Belle Époque. As Moore moved from the traditional formalism of the academy to the ritualized spectacle of the boulevard and, finally, to the intimate space of the café, his perspective changed from the traditional to the modern. He paid less attention to concrete representations of people and objects and more to their subjective meaning. A young man hungry for experience who openly took advantage of every opportunity provided him, Moore was transformed, along with the city he admired. In the context of the society of the Nouvelle Athènes, Moore is remembered as a type of decadent aesthete and a dandy (Crespelle, pp. 137–138). His outward appearance and manners reflected the world of the boulevards, yet Moore was emotionally attracted to the Montmartre avant-garde. Though he could not blend into the environment, he was able to transport many of its political ideas and aesthetic principles back to Ireland and England when he returned.

Moore witnessed France's remarkable transformation from a monarchist state. The evolution was an historic achievement, making France, alone among all the major European nations, a republic. The spirit of republicanism had remained strong in France since the Revolution of 1789. When Moore arrived, the Grand Revolution, less than a century away, was still remembered as the greatest popular revolt in modern memory. Aristocrats around the world recalled with horror the power and savagery of the masses, and the people revelled in their moments of power over the king. The glory of the First Republic was recalled during the Revolution of 1830, which had so inspired the Romantic writers whom Moore admired; more recently, it had propelled the Revolution of 1848 and the founding of the Second Republic. The last revolt had had repercussions across Europe, even as far as Ireland. It had introduced the spectre of the proletariat to the conservators of the old regime. Napoleon III's *coup d'état* had betrayed the democratic processes of the Second Republic, and the framers of the Third were much more cautious in selecting their chief executive. As the royalist parties fought for control of the throne through the 1870s, the rural population steadily became more republican in outlook. When President MacMahon impulsively dissolved the National Assembly and called for national elections in 1877, the monarchist cause was effectively voted out of office. The situation was different in Ireland, where few among the agricultural poor owned land, but Moore could not have failed to be aware of the political transformation around him. The habitués of the Nouvelle Athènes were bourgeois republicans of long standing. Both of his heroes, Manet and Degas, had fought for the government during the Prussian seige of 1870. Degas attributed his blindness to the chill he received during that hard winter, and when Manet was reunited with his family in the south of France after the hostilities had ceased, he was gaunt and in need of rest.

For these men, politics represented more than a lively topic for discussion or the cause of war; it affected their daily lives and their work. Degas, in deriding the landscape impressionists, revealed an ingrained fear of the authoritarian regime: 'If I were the government', he quipped, 'I'd have the police watch landscapists' (Schneider, p. 137). The group of the Nouvelle Athènes represented the *juste milieu*, the carefully trodden middle path which was to be the way of the Third Republic. Their political hero was Léon Gambetta, the flamboyant republican who had eluded the Prussians by escaping from beseiged Paris in a hot air balloon. Gambetta was known to Manet; he was the former secretary to Manet's cousin, Jules de Jouy.[12] Manet had observed the collapse of the Second Empire with personal interest. In his final attempt to save his empire in January of 1870, Napoleon III had turned it into a parliamentary regime, headed by Emile Ollivier, Manet's companion in Venice seventeen years earlier (Perruchot, p. 175). Manet was convinced that Gambetta was the only person who could save his country. His overwhelming admiration for the charismatic politician inspired him to resume painting after the Commune and, naturally, he pursued Gambetta as a subject. Unfortunately Gambetta was not impressed with Manet's painting and refused to cooperate. Furious at his idol's rejection, Manet exclaimed, 'All these Republicans are birds of a feather. Mention art to them, and you'll find they're the worst sort of reactionary' (Perruchot, p. 183). Manet's generalization about republican esteem of art contained some truth, for the Third Republic did not support a Salon des Refusés in the 1870s. However, Manet's old friend, the republican Antonin Proust, was elected Deputy from Niort in 1876; he proved more supportive. Proust championed the cause of the arts in the Assembly, offering his personal assistance to Manet. He sat for three separate portraits by Manet, in 1856, 1877, and 1880. In 1879, the year he executed Moore's portrait, Manet also painted the dramatic pose of another Montmartre republican, Georges Clemenceau. Finally, in 1881 when Gambetta was the new prime minister and Proust his Minister of Fine Arts, Gambetta succeeded in nominating Manet for the Legion of Honour (Schneider, p. 172).

As Manet's eventual acceptance by the government suggests, the superficially revolutionary world of the Nouvelle Athènes café where Moore apprenticed was comparatively conservative. Politics were important to them because the tyranny of official opinion deprived them of a living; unable to exhibit, they were unlikely to sell their paintings. The men who frequented the café were generally traditional in their personal lives, embodying the propriety of the French bourgeoisie. They indulged in none of the excesses exemplified by Baudelaire and Verlaine. They were, however, daring in their art, delving into the very processes of creation with exploratory zeal. This is the critical education which Moore seems to have enjoyed in the café. His articles on modern painting vividly depict the artist at work, describing the action of brush and colours with such understanding that he emerges as a participant and not merely a critic.

The effect that the political and social environment of Paris had on Moore is, at first glance, less evident. Moore was young when he arrived in Paris – twenty-one; he was not yet thirty when he left in 1880. He had come to the city first to study painting, then to become a writer; his explicit goal never was to analyse the political scene. He spent his time with his own kind, middle-class artists and intellectuals, visiting the salons that were opened to him by letters of introduction from his family. He was not attracted to the Irish revolutionary, John O'Leary, when he met him in Paris, as he found the Fenian and the Irish community in Paris not carefree enough.[13] From that encounter, he gravitated toward the *haute* bourgeoisie, but the meeting with O'Leary must have made an impression upon his unconscious memory. As a young man who aggressively devoured experience, Moore undoubtedly filed away for later recall many observations during his early Paris years. The political situation in Ireland during the decade following Moore's return in 1880 bore many correlations to events that had transpired during his seven years in Paris. The Phoenix Park murder of the new Chief Secretary (Lord Frederick Cavendish) and his undersecretary on May 6, 1882 evoked a governmental response similar to that which followed the violence of the Paris Commune of 1871. Indeed, although the murders were single acts of urban terrorism, perpetrated against specific individuals, the assassins had been inspired by the anarchist polemics of the Commune. Both expressed bitter political opposition to the existing government and frustration with moderate reform as a way to resolve political differences. The Commune instilled a deep and abiding fear of the urban proletariat in the minds of land-holders throughout France; consequently it affected legislation enacted by their representatives. The Land League had the same impact upon Irish landholders. The monarchists elected to the French National Assembly ended the modest liberalization that Napoleon III had undertaken and sought to return the nation to order. Likewise, the moderate progress made by Parnell in Ireland, consolidated in the Kilmainham Compact, was seriously undercut by the murders. English reaction reinforced the repressive Coercion measures and forced Parnell to rebuild his party. The subsequent years were a time of gradual realignment and of difficult negotiation for Parnell, during which he eventually attained a level of admiration in both England and Ireland that echoed the personal popularity enjoyed by Gambetta in France.[14]

Many of these Irish scenes must have provided a sense of *déjà vu* for Moore. Life in Paris had given him an education both in national politics and in the many ways in which individuals might respond to events around them. Foreign tourists and wealthy residents of the Champs-Elysées had been relatively free to ignore traditional social realities and to create their own. The French artists of Montmartre, however, could not be so passive. Perhaps more fundamental than their material struggle, their aesthetic quest provided a critical paradigm that Moore was able to use reflexively when confronted by Irish events. In Paris he had absorbed the rituals of political discourse and art; in Ireland he employed them in the service of the Gaelic League and the Irish literary renaissance. Dublin provided many meeting places that attracted the politically and artistically conscious clientele with which Moore liked to converse, according to the rhetorical rules he had learned in the Parisian salon, studio, and café. He used his Paris years profitably; he equipped himself with an eclectic critical approach to both life and work; he collected a storehouse of descriptions, anecdotes, and trivia upon which he would draw for decades to follow.

NOTES

1 Frederick William John Hemmings, *Culture and Society in France, 1848–1898; Dissidents and Philistines* (London: B.T. Batsford, 1971), p. 194. All subsequent references are to this edition.
2 For a complete description of their work, see David H. Pinkney, *Napoleon III and the Rebuilding of Paris* (Princeton: Princeton University Press, 1972).
3 See Robert Burnand, *La Vie quotidienne en France de 1870 à 1900* (Paris: Hachette, 1947).
4 George Moore, *Confessions of a Young Man*, ed. Susan Dick (Montreal and London: McGill-Queen's University Press, 1972), p. 55. All subsequent references are to this edition.
5 Edmondo De Amicis, *Studies of Paris* (New York, Putnam, 1879), p. 243. All subsequent references are to this edition.
6 Augustus J. Hare, *Walks in Paris* (New York: Routledge, 1890) pp. 338–339.
7 'Paris, the egalitarian city, the democratic city par excellence, wanted to have a promenade within its boundaries which would represent and serve the needs of the crowd, which would belong to everyone . . . she lovingly created the true promenade of the future, the veritable garden of the emancipated city, the boulevards.' Adolphe Joanne, *Paris Illustréen 1870 et 1877; Guide de l'étranger et du parisien*, Third Ed., (Paris: Hachette, 1878), pp. 43–44. All subsequent references are to this edition.

8 Harry Sutherland Edwards, *Old and New Paris; Its History, its People, and its Places* (London: Cassell, 1893), I, p. 103.

9 George Augusts Sala, *Paris Herself Again* (London: Golden Galley Press Limited, 1948), p. 74. All subsequent references are to this edition.

10 Pierre Schneider, *The World of Manet, 1832–1883* (New York: Time-Life Books, 1968), p. 135. All subsequent references are to this edition.

11 Jean-Paul Crespelle, *Degas et son Monde* (Paris: Presses de al Cité, 1972), pp. 133–138. All subsequent references are to this edition.

12 Henri Perruchot, *Manet*, trans. Humphrey Hare, ed. Jean Ellsmoor (Cleveland and New York: World, 1963), p. 175. All subsequent references are to this edition.

13 Joseph Hone, *The Life of George Moore* (New York: Macmillan, 1936), p. 55.

14 T.A. Jackson, *Ireland Her Own; An Outline History of the Irish Struggle for National Freedom and Independence*, ed. C. Desmond Greaves (London: Lawrence and Wishart, 1976), pp. 331–349. Note also the discussions of Parnell and indications of English attitudes in Virginia Woolf's *The Years*.

GEORGE MOORE'S DUBLIN

JAMES LIDDY

Dublin is an eternal city, a city transfixed in the movement from empire to imagination with a democratic heart. It is a city lavished on by history; self-burning with long time-wraps which lie on top of each other like earthworks. One age can be peeled away to reveal another; one set of manners is tied to a hidden drawing room. Even the casual visitor has the sensation that afternoons can be very long in Dublin, as indeterminate perhaps as hundreds of years. As a child coming to the metropolis in the forties I had the knowledge that the streets, the shops, and the hotels had done the same business for an aeon. That city of war and aftermath pulsed with an identity that still performs for me as the essential Dublin, stretching up to the somewhat shape-changed city of today and retreating in a tide of nostalgia to the eighteenth century. What the city has developed in these centuries seems to be an active consciousness, a sort of summonable-by-writer aerial view of itself – which at the same time takes the form of a deaerating process so that in descriptions of itself the environs and centre of the city become less ethereal and more physically founded. So it was that I, a County Wexford child, discovered in his journeys to this alluring, solid place a perception and perambulating method of thought that is, was, and ever will be George Moore's Dublin. Certainly I am never allowed to forget the fairy godfather or witch doctor that stood at the first door into mythic reality – nor can I ever cease from interpreting a pattern that will reincarnate elements of such a figure. When anyone hails such a site there can be no formation of a farewell.

That I share Dublin with millions who have never walked its pavements is, however, a matter of record to everyone who reads modern literature. Dublin is known through its writers as Paris is known through its painters and the island of Bali through its dancers. Writers have given the city of Dublin to the rest of the world; each literary artist has described a different aspect of the urbs. Out of the fictive imagination each has created, alongside the real city each inhabits, a secondary city. For Swift, the central area known as the Liberties was his personal mitreless purgatory with only the relief of protest. For Joyce, the whole city was a matrix from which the significations of reality flowed. For O'Casey it became the mother-city of generous social and communal impulses. Behan revelled in the mother milk of its humanity and classless spirit. For George Moore it was a city in which to adopt a persona and to make a raid on the next stage of the articulate. When he was a child living in Moore Hall in Mayo, it was sometimes a stopping-off place to and back from the parliamentary city of London; sometimes a holiday place, a strange and smaller London, to which he went on excursions with father and brother. As a young man of the landowning class, intensely interested in the personal aspects of a dying feudalism, Moore went alone to the city whose centre was Dublin Castle during fortune-hunting season: this was the Dublin he depicted in *A Drama in Muslin*. For Moore the established writer in his late forties whose books had been published in France, England, and the United States, the city glinted as a desert with patches of fertile soil about to be irrigated by Yeats's Literary Renaissance and Hyde's Gaelic Revival. It also shone as an arena to exhibit his observation and form. It must have struck him as an ideal site for the making of a Sacred Book, as envisaged by his friends, the Symbolists.

Dublin at the turn of the century, the Dublin of both Renaissance and Revival, was a city of slightly less than half a million people, economically dominated by brewing, biscuit-making, general industry, and the export of cattle. Architecturally, it combined fine Georgian squares, domes, and public buildings with slums. Though the earlier bucks and the later dandies had gone, it retained a raffish suburban feeling and apocalyptic airs. James Joyce wrote in a letter, 'When you remember that Dublin has been a capital for thousands of years, that it is the 'second city' of the British Empire, that it is nearly three times as big as Venice, it seems strange that no artist has given it to the world'.[1] (This of course was not strictly true, but there occurs a large time gap between Swift and Joyce and Moore, the two artists who were to bring Dublin forth again.) Living in Dublin was always like living in the years preceding the end of the world, with the proviso that a new city was about to be born that would not be much changed. The same crowds would flow down its streets. The twentieth-century city was, to use a native phrase, 'black with people'. An anonymous writer has described it, 'One soon gets accustomed to meeting drunks of both sexes at all hours of the day. It is not an uncommon sight to come across a woman at mid-day lying absolutely inert in the middle of the road or pathway, or clutching at an iron railway, motionless as a statue, unable to stir.'[2] The words provide a vivid illustration of the familiar 'centre of paralysis' – but the new centre was beginning to cast interesting shadows. Out at the Royal Dublin Society show grounds in Ballsbridge, Dublin citizens were parting with their shillings for the novelty of a ride in a motor car, far from 'the shores of a misted lake among a dim, half-effaced peopled'.[3]

When Moore, having moved from London, arrived in Dublin in 1901 with his furniture, paintings, and Aubusson carpet, it was for a variety of reasons. A prominent motive was to get away from the hue and cry of the Boer war; but another was the need to remake an Irish identity by joining the twin movements that were setting up prospects of a post-Parnell Ireland. One of these movements was the Literary Renaissance, then giving practical impetus to the idea of a National Theatre, an adventure that Moore believed he could help with his own experience and theatrical connexions in England. As important for the returned expatriate loomed the Gaelic Movement and the necessity for it to pass the first revival stage into an active consideration of the possibilities of a modern literature in the national language. This second cause especially attracted Moore on arrival. He had packed his bags and vacated his London apartment to come to Ireland 'in the hope of reviving the language of the tribe that used to come down from the rim of blue hills that could be seen from the windows enclosing the plain, to invade Dublin and to be repulsed by different garrisons of the Pale'.[4]

The man who arrived in Dublin in 1901 was a different Moore, a maturer figure in a more progressive Ireland than the man who had known Dublin (and was known through his Dublin associations) during the 1880s and before. Then he had seen the city through the windows of the Shelbourne, so to speak. The main character in *A Drama in Muslin*, Alice Barton, had resided there during the 1882 Castle season. The city of the Lord Lieutenant, set in the context of a seedy, second-rate colony, had then been Moore's writing ground. Around the corner from the Shelbourne, at the end of a vista, stood the epitome of provincial autocracy: 'See the pot-hatted Gigmen of the Kildare Street Club'![5] The Shelbourne Hotel itself, founded in 1824, remodelled into its present elegance in 1866, had flourished even more in the Edwardian decade than it had in the sunset of the dear queen. Its nineteenth-century spirit looked over the Stephen's Green quarter of the south city then as it does now (the vast – for Dublin – building has been caught atmospherically in a phrase by Elizabeth Bowen, in her book on the hotel, 'Tall as a cliff but more genial . . .'[6]). The Green he saw from the Shelbourne was spacious

Central Dublin, from *Thom's Directory* map of 1901.

for a packed city; it must have created a sense of structure and form for Moore in different parts of his career. The hotel itself must have given him his other sense (which undoubtedly Moore Hall additionally provided) of rising to style and greatness. Bowen wrote of the Shelbourne, 'It stands for grandeur'.[7] At its height during Horse Show Week and international rugby nights it glowed like a modern Tara in the local imagination. In 1901 AE obtained a house for Moore around the corner, 4 Upper Ely Place – convenient for lunch, tea, or a meeting in the hotel drawing room, dominated by the great Bossi mantlepiece. Thus the novelist walked, talked, and ate (sometimes those insufferable omelettes) in the centre of the city of both old and new residences. His newly wedded panorama, that of resident rather than visitor, consisted of hotel and close by eighteenth-century townhouses, up an impressive cul-de-sac.

The book Moore made out of his ten Irish years, 1901–1911, is partly a source book about Moore, partly about Dublin. *Hail and Farewell* lacks the detail of Joyce's better-known *Ulysses*, the wide cross-sectioning. But a certain part of the city between the Grand Canal and the Liffey could be fished from its pages, as other parts could be built from Joyce's fiction. Walking and conversation, not reading, became Moore's mode of learning about Dublin; he studied daily these streets of the upper crust and inner city. No writer – perhaps not even Joyce – has looked at the south side squares and adjoining thoroughfares with more exquisite observation. 'The rickety lodging-house appearance of Baggot Street'[8] is balanced against 'The sun sets nowhere so beautifully as it does at the end of Baggot Street'.[9] Tree-lined, a stone's throw from hotel and new domicile, the vista is one of the many in this area that Moore admired with his painter's eye. Rupert Hart-Davis remarks in his preface to Moore's letters to Lady Cunard, 'Few writers have so tightly interwoven fact and fiction as George Moore did in his autobiographical works. Naturally inaccurate in detail, he would transpose dates, events, and people in any way that suited his own purpose'.[10] In the phrase, entering the Shelbourne 'as any stranger from America might',[11] he conjured up a thousand and one Irish-American nights among the German waiters that he had pictured twenty years before in *A Drama in Muslin*, standing around the winter garden on the old landing watching the debutantes go off into the Castle night. The Green is the pleasure garden of the hotel in which Moore set his memorable early encounter with Yeats. Moore already had in contemplation the Anti-Sacred Book that would attempt to desacrilise the Celtic Renaissance; he watched Yeats's energy and intentness. In the city

Moore remained the Mayo-trained lover of nature; as a child he had rambled around that countryside with the jockeys and stable boys (in fact, he had roamed freely by horse and boat – the lakes were higher then – and he and brother Maurice sometimes had gone by boat as far as Cong to picnic with Willy and Oscar Wilde). To this native pastoral lore, Moore added something of the nature-worshipping of the English Romantic poets. So he was able to note, when talking with Yeats in Stephen's Green, that the leader of the Renaissance lacked in his make-up what fed and created the early Gaelic literature: springtime tree and bird. Moore's alliance with a non-city instinct, the ideological pattern in his thought of opening up to a 'garden of life', enabled him to do more than penetrate Dublin with sly side-glances. It led him towards comic values in the book he was planning.

When did Moore conceive himself to be a comic figure? When did he decide that he himself was a major element in this comedy, spiced with revenge for the ambiguous invitations of Yeats and Martyn to come over and help the cause? In Ireland the price of believing in something is trouble compensated for by a profoundly liberating sense of the comic. Moore spent his last four years in Dublin, drafting his trilogy, after the interior collapse of his idealistic hopes for a new cultural scene. He had to protect himself from the idea of uselessness. Besides, all his life Moore protested, not just for art's sake but also for protest's sake. No wonder one of the great comic melodies in *Hail and Farewell* is the refrain in which he makes himself a Protestant. Being a dissident was his major forte; Herbert Howarth uses the phrase 'crystallization of his dissidence' to describe the year 1899–1911.[12] John Eglinton (William K. Magee) estimates that the moment of comic realization, spawning the truth of the work, occurred about half way through Moore's Dublin period. Eglinton sees the voice of common sense inevitably leading this way; he suggests that Moore left Ireland in 1911 for literary reasons (what other reasons could there be for Moore?): he had become 'well established' and had exhausted his subject as far as comedy and farce were concerned.[13]

Moore achieved status (and resentment) as a writer on and about the Irish scene because he could 'take off' in his style the categories of public life. His use of direct speech, as in his account of the famous launching dinner at the Shelbourne, is uniformly brilliant. In addition to Yeats and Hyde, we are here introduced to John O'Leary, the Fenian chief and literary enthusiast of the period; T.W. Rolleston, poet and critic known for a single lyric, 'The Dead at Clonmacnoise'; T.P. Gill, editor of the lively Dublin newspaper,

The Daily Express; Standish O'Grady, translator and adapter from the Gaelic of heroic tales; Fr. Finlay, University economist; and Sir Horace Plunkett, agrarian revolutionary. It is only with the ladies in *Hail and Farewell* that Moore's inquisitiveness fails; apart from that which he trains on Lady Gregory, Moore's hard focus on society weakens. This is so perhaps because ladies were for him naturally part of the private life. Women he eschewed here with deliberation. *Hail and Farewell* sizzles as a celebration of men and their world; appropriate for a country where the masculine will is open. On the other hand the novelist found great relish in feasting on the bones of male victims. He cuts up like a surgeon the brain and bodies of Gill and Fr. Finlay; he excels in insult and in demonically puffed-up half truths. He says of Horace Plunkett that he 'fears to meet anyone with a sense of humour; he dreads laughter as a cat dreads cold water'.[14] He refers in a long carefully abusive passage to the 'soft and peaty Hyde'.[15] But these skirmishes – a smiling paying of scores as with Joyce – are wound around an environment of a city that is presented as benign and autumnal. The city was for him an habitable image, a resort for insult as well as loneliness. He liked the mass weight of it though he personally sunk into the rich status of a 'private eye'. Of Paris, Moore had written, 'Once my youth moved through thy whiteness, O City, and its dreams lay down to dream in the freedom of thy fields'![16] The evanescent spiritual state of Dublin city life that sings to us in *Hail and Farewell* had its contrasts with what Moore had written of Paris in *Confessions of a Young Man* and *A Modern Lover* and of London in *Esther Waters*.

George Moore's Dublin days were patterned; in one respect he had the soul of a clock face. Joseph Hone declared that he had a busy social life; this may have been true earlier but soon company dwindled. John Eglinton wrote, 'He soon began to be left to himself in Dublin, with a contracted circle of intimates, of whom rather unwillingly at first I became one'.[17] Moore's civic style tended to concentrate on neighbour and landlord bashing. Dublin mocks the mocker; comic virtue is catching. Moore installed himself in 4, Upper Ely Place (which is not really Ely Place at all but the back part of the street that leads nowhere except to a nuns' garden). This section was locked with a gate and known as Smith's buildings. Gogarty gives an account of a Saturday dinner party in Moore's house and notes the deadly quiet of the street: 'Neither vehicles nor foot passengers entered Ely Place after sundown'.[18] For a small additional rent a garden was leased with the house; it had, according to its tenant, the largest apple tree in Ireland. Moore was particularly delighted with the chatter of washerwomen in the cottages behind Ely Place. The street was comfortably Protestant; the rector the Archbishop of Dublin referred him to after receiving his letter of conversion was the Reverend Gilbert Mahaffy, who lived at 'No. 13 Ely Place, one door from the great iron gateway that divides my little cul-de-sac from Ely Place'. . . .[19] Other neighbours were Sir Thornley Stoker, the surgeon with whom Moore quarreled; Cunningham, the publican, whose suicide he chronicles in *A Story Teller's Holiday*; and Gogarty who watched Moore with deadly (and posthumous) malice from the close proximity of this box-like area.

Moore's working day had the regularity of an office job. He wrote usually from 10:30 to 4:00. The business atmosphere must have been reinforced by the choice of dictation to a secretary as the method of composition. Working through dictation and thereafter further working orally from a typed manuscript had been his practice since at least *Esther Waters*.[20] He often went for a stroll after work, perhaps like a magpie on the streets, picking up bits and pieces for his current page. Occasionally he played tennis, wearing a bowler hat. After dinner he would saunter down past the Shelbourne to the National Library in Kildare Street, to catch up with his reading and to talk about St. Paul or some other hot Gospel subject with his friend John Eglinton. On Saturdays he gave dinner to his friends, a better dinner than they were accustomed to. He held an 'evening' afterwards for his two special friends, Eglinton and AE. Basically he had one circle: the literary men such as Seamus O'Sullivan, T.W. Rolleston, Padraic Colum, Oliver Gogarty, Kuno Meyer – Synge came once. Moore, in his late Dublin period, seemed like a caged animal, intent on a subject matter – the life of his city – which remained suspicious of him. But Moore never lacked friends; he was ever gracious, gregarious, and (when he wanted to be) sweet-hearted.

Moore went out also; a favourite excursion was to Michele Esposito's house where his host played the piano recital he had given previously at the Royal Dublin Society. Esposito reflected the musical culture of Dubin at this time, as did Shaw's early music criticism. He had come from Italy some years before and taught pianoforte at the Royal Irish Academy of Music; he had attractive daughters with whom James Joyce was acquainted. In general Moore's life, however, followed the role of the artist-celibate, the consummate hermit. He could clown his loneliness effectively, but Dublin responded by going elsewhere for its fun and wit. It kissed and did not tell Moore. It is difficult to judge the long contest between Moore and the city he parried with. From some there arose a fierce reaction to his personality and ways, especially after the publication of the trilogy. Not everyone took the public episode of his conversion to the Reformed Faith as a piece of playacting; he was greatly disliked for it. To Susan Mitchell he was a 'Donnybrook Fair Irishman'.[21] Gogarty asserts, 'Pernickety was the name that described Moore'.[22] His effect was more accurately set down by Harold Acton, friend of Lady Cunard, who writes of Moore's 'snowy crest and droopy moustache, his blue marble nursery eyes and cherubic complexion . . . his bubbling hot dish of a voice'.[23] These characteristics might have been counterproductive in a city in which the definition of vice is a bad pose. Dublin knew Moore was made, not mad. Joyce spoke for the city in his famous lines from 'Gas from a Burner',

'. . . Written by Moore, a genuine gent
    That lived on his property's ten per cent'.[24]

As Patrick McCarthy has demonstrated in another essay in this volume, between George Moore and James Joyce there were correspondences; it follows there were correspondences also between the Dublin each treated possessively in his art even as he rejected it as a permanent address. The great presences they both hated together swim passionately into their work. Moore is more prosy about this obsession; 'Two dominant notes in my character – an original hatred of my native country, and a brutal loathing of the religion I was brought up in'.[25] The comparison is insistent between the two: each attempts to fly by the same nets, nationality and religion. Today, Dublin is Joyce's city and, to a lesser extent, Moore's. The grandchildren of Joyce's contemporaries run the professions, politics, the colleges, the business world with the great-grandchildren of Moore's tenants. Moore's own world (to which at times he was so aloof) continues diminished in the clubs, the Royal Dublin Society events, the tea-time horsey babble in the Shelbourne. If Joyce's demonic participation in the twentieth century contrasts with Moore's faded nineteenth century baiting of it, Moore stays readable and interesting. Dublin lives as a real place in his pages; perhaps it should have been more of a 'dream city' as Moore Hall in Mayo was a 'dream house'. His power of manipulating his experience and memory becomes triumphant; looking back, Patrick Kavanagh notes, 'There has been no successful autobiography. George Moore's is good because he invented his friends.'[26]

Looking back also, Cyril Connolly sees Moore as being primarily of the school of Dublin, with Yeats, Joyce, Synge, and Stephens. 'Their aim was to discover what blend of Anglo-Irish and French would give them an explosive that would knock the pundits of London off their padded chairs. All had lived in Paris, and all had absorbed French culture'.[27] (An estimate, probably, more Anglo-Irish than that of the Anglo-Irish themselves!) Today's School of Dublin looks less to London and Paris, more to New York and San Francisco; the culture of the latter is adapted to knock the pundits of the former from their chairs. Yet re-reading Moore after many years, I come upon that word-light that revivifies a complex of first feelings, and I realize that a writer has described my home. I come upon that happiest of civilized intuitions, that someone has been there before me. I can say with Elizabeth Bowen, 'For me, who was a Dublin child, the Shelbourne remains the prototype of all large hotels. . .'[28] As a child I entered its lounge, restaurant, bar, with my parents, and knew with them Fred, the last of the German waiters. The tableware was as elegant, the food as uninteresting as years before, in Moore's time: in the large lounge (no longer alas a drawing room) the mix of religion and money was becoming more Catholic than Protestant. The Bossi mantlepiece passed away with Captain Jury, and the hotel became a Forte Trust House. The writing room turned into the horseshoe bar, conveniently near to Government Buildings for cabinet ministers to drink double brandies in. Outside remained the Green of Moore and Yeats and Joyce and me – but was Irish pond, bush, duck, and ornamental bridge ever better captured than by Moore? Surely the day will come when his bust too will dream there; an apology for the 1923 burning of Moore Hall.

Patrick Kavanagh memorably pairs Moore and Joyce as being 'truely Irish and Catholic and European'.[29] Increasingly in the EEC Dublin has this ambience; it supplants Yeats's eighteenth-century model. The part of Dublin that seems not quite time-proof passes on, is passed over. Moore's and Joyce's city survives; I amble down their somewhat altered thoroughfares. Their art is laughter-evoking, magnificent caprice in the sense of Nabokov's question, 'Isn't all art whimsical, from Shakespeare to Joyce'?[30] Such comic spirits cannot be repressed; they will always accompany us with rain and gold whiskey, the colour of eternity.

NOTES

1   Richard Ellmann, ed., *Selected Letters of James Joyce* (New York: Viking, 1975), p. 78.

2 *Dublin: Explorations and Reflections by an Englishman*, (Dublin: Maunsel, 1918), p. 69.
3 George Moore, *Memoirs of My Dead Life* (London: Heinemann, 1921), p. 6.
4 George Moore, *Salve* (London: Heinemann, 1912), p. 9.
5 George Moore, *A Drama in Muslin* (London: Vizetelly, 1886), p. 159.
6 Elizabeth Bowen, *The Shelbourne Hotel* (New York: Knopf, 1951), p. 3.
7 Bowen, p. 10.
8 Moore, *Salve*, p. 205.
9 *Salve*, p. 206.
10 Rupert Hart-Davis, ed., *George Moore Letters 1895–1933 to Lady Cunard* (London: Hart-Davis, 1957), p. 11.
11 George Moore, *Ave* (London: Heinemann, 1911), p. 98.
12 Herbert Howarth, 'Dublin 1899–1911: The Enthusiasm of a Prodigal,' in *George Moore's Mind and Art*, ed. Graham Owens (New York: Barnes & Noble, 1970), p. 90.
13 John Eglinton, 'Recollections of George Moore,' in *The Man of Wax*, ed. Douglas A. Hughes (New York: New York University Press, 1971), p. 28.
14 George Moore, *Vale* (London: Heinemann, 1914), p. 207.
15 *Vale*, p. 247.
16 George Moore, *Memoirs of My Dead Life*, pp. 29–30.
17 John Eglinton, *The Man of Wax*, p. 18.
18 Oliver St. John Gogarty, *It isn't This Time of Year at All* (New York: Doubleday, 1954), p. 137.
19 Moore, *Salve*, p. 367.
20 Graham Owens, 'Melodic Line in Narrative,' in *George Moore's Mind and Art*, ed. Graham Owens (New York: Barnes and Noble, 1970), p. 102.
21 Susan Mitchell, *George Moore*, (Dublin: Maunsel, 1916), p. 107.
22 Oliver St. John Gogarty, *It Isn't This Time of Year at All*, p. 133.
23 Harold Acton, 'George Moore and the Cunard Family,' *The London Magazine*, 5, 3, (March 1958), pp. 54, 57.
24 Harry Levin, ed., *The Portable James Joyce* (New York: Viking, 1947), p. 661.
25 George Moore, *Confessions of a Young Man* (Montreal and London: McGill-Queens Univ., 1972), p. 109.
26 Patrick Kavanagh, *Lapped Furrows* (New York: Peter Kavanagh Hand Press, 1969), p. 227.
27 Cyril Connolly, *Enemies of Promise* (London: Penguin, 1961), p. 42.
28 Elizabeth Bowen, *The Shelbourne Hotel*, p. 10.
29 Patrick Kavanagh, 'George Moore's Dublin', *The Irish Times*, 13 June 1965, p. v.
30 Simon Karlinsky, ed., *The Nabokov-Wilson Letters* (New York: Harper & Row, 1979), pp. 330–331.

PRIVATE MOORE, PUBLIC MOORE: THE EVIDENCE OF THE LETTERS

ROBERT STEPHEN BECKER

'She'll vish there wos more', said Sam Weller in *Pickwick Papers*, 'and that's the great art o' letter writin' '. By Sam's charming standard of epistolary art, one could hesitate before rating George Moore a success. For a collected edition of his correspondence now in progress, over six thousand manuscript and printed letters have been located, and the number is growing. The earliest letter was written in his eleventh year, and the last just eleven days before his death at the age of eighty. The editor who intends to gain control of this vast literary record may be tempted to exclaim after William Blake: 'Enough! or Too Much'.

Blake's proverb was a celebration of abundance, so the exclamation is fitting. In his large, flowing handwriting, compressed at times by the urgency of expression, Moore addressed a variety of relations, friends, associates, and enemies. Through his letters he has encouraged posterity to become intimately acquainted with his private and public character and with aspects of cultural history in the Victorian, Edwardian, and Georgian periods.

The personality which rises from a reading of the letters is complex, but clearly organized. Moore's roles as a correspondent fall neatly into various categories reflecting his professional and personal interests. Depending on the document at hand, he may be viewed as a creative writer, critical theorist, or theatre director; an Irish landlord or gentleman in the higher circles of English society; a son, sibling, perhaps even a father; a friend, or a lover. Common to all these roles are consistency of purpose and intellectual integrity contributing to what Moore himself regarded as his exceptional, sometimes problematic individuality. 'I was born, I live and I shall die a peculiar man', he told his mother in 1883, '– I could not be commonplace were I to try' (MS. National Library of Ireland).

Owing to individual points of view and what were construed, during his lifetime, as peculiar objectives, Moore frequently found himself in conflict with artistic conventions and historical trends. The conflicts sometimes restrained, sometimes intensified his ambitions and certainly helped in the creation of his achievement. As a man of letters he advocated French literary theory in the first twenty years of his career. While alignment with the avant-garde has now placed him in the tradition of modern English literature, in his time he was considered a pornographer and a decadent. In the years leading to and following the turn of the century, he promoted reforms in the theatre now embodied in the modern conception of stagecraft. Again, however, in his time he was often ridiculed and reviled for having slandered English drama. Henry Irving reflected influential public opinion when he referred to Moore as 'a spiteful and irresponsible writer . . . the hater and scorner of the stage . . . a tasteless trifler . . . a blockhead' (*The Times*, 3 October 1888). As an Irish landlord he inherited problems stemming from agrarian reform. Despite his vocal Liberal sympathies and the fact that he did not exploit his property for extravagant income, he lived to see the entire estate pass from his family's ownership and Moore Hall, the place of his birth, burned. As a man of social standing he fraternized with powerful members of the English aristocracy, but he was denied the knighthood he apparently coveted. Conflicts such as these are illuminated throughout the correspondence. They help to place Moore in a diversified context and throw valuable personal light on his cultural background.

THE CREATIVE WRITER

My Dear Mama
   I made my first Communion this morning. You must send me some things. Please to send me my writing-case. [MS. National Library of Ireland].

So begins Moore's first surviving letter, dated 28 March 1863. It is tempting to interpret a connection between Holy Communion and the sudden call for writing materials. Though in private Moore doubted the existence of God, in his writings he was vitally concerned about Christianity.
   Lady Hemphill informed Joseph Hone in 1935 that in Paris in the 1870s, Moore was known as 'Lucifer'. James Davis recorded in the *Sporting Times* that in London during the early 1880s, Moore was called 'Pagan'. These nicknames suited the author of the juvenile *Flowers of Passion* (1877) and *Pagan Poems* (1881), but the work which may be regarded as Moore's first attempt at serious literature, *Martin Luther* (1879), addressed the topics of Protestant Reformation and the implications of modern Christian morality.
   Christian themes grew to occupy a central place in the Moore

canon. The heroines of *A Mummer's Wife* (1884) and *Esther Waters* (1894) shared a fundamentalist orientation from childhood which inhibited, in the former case prevented, the achievement of a wholesome, mature happiness. The jarring influence of Protestant doctrine had its Catholic counterpart in other novels. When Olive Schreiner resided at the Convent of St. Leonard's, Hastings, in 1885, she transmitted an account of convent life to Moore, who adapted it for the opening scenes of *A Drama in Muslin* (1886). The passages provoked a warm controversy in the English Catholic press, to which Moore contributed a letter defending himself. Roman Catholic dogma became a pivotal element in *A Mere Accident* (1887), *Evelyn Innes* (1898), *Sister Teresa* (1901), *The Untilled Field* (1903) and *The Lake* (1905). In these volumes Moore, as the narrator, might be regarded as a kind of Barabbas, unbelieving yet obsessed with belief. Following the amusing, if sometimes vindictive, attack on Catholicism in *Hail and Farewell* (1911–1914), he squared up to the subject in *The Brook Kerith* (1916), a retelling of the life of Christ in which Christ himself is secularized. In his last novel to examine Christian themes, *Héloise and Abélard* (1921), Moore returned to his first concentration on the Protestant Reformation, the source of which he discovered in the medieval philosopher Pierre Abélard.

The existence of God is never denied in either the surviving correspondence or the literature. In lieu of a missing definitive statement by Moore, it is safe for his interpreters to characterize him as an agnostic rather than as an atheist. He was not seriously troubled by the problem of God's existence. The manner of worshipping an assumed existence did, however, ignite his imagination.

'Other men have wives, children, religion, God,' Moore wrote to Lady Cunard in 1906; 'I have my star, an ideal, my ideal of light, loveliness and grace which I follow always . . .' (MS. Sir Sacheverell Sitwell). For Moore, the idea of divinity could be adequately understood as the object of man's most profound aspirations. Whether divinity be an omnipotent monarch enthroned in heaven, an intellectual or aesthetic preoccupation, or the simple human harmony suggested by a woman's love, it was bound to shape man's values and conduct. Throughout his career he wrote as though a true comprehension of religious practice and belief was one of his primary artistic obligations. Through religious thinking both he and many of his fictional characters set aside the accidental mask imposed by birth and experience. They became more themselves, whether fruitfully or tragically, as life was unified with imagination.

In 1916, worried that Shane Leslie would describe him as a Catholic in *The End of a Chapter*, Moore informed the younger author: 'I never was a Catholic and am sorry that you are because your intellect will perish in dogma if you persist in it' (MS. National Library of Ireland). In a letter to Shane's mother written six years earlier, Moore had explained that Shane's

Catholicism was the natural mistake of a young man who desires the nationalization of Ireland. He did not stop to ask if Catholicism and nationality were compatible. Catholicism aims at cosmopolitanism – the very thing he hates, and wherever it goes the intellect perishes. Vienna, the largest Catholic city in the world, is frivolous, cosmopolitan and illiterate beyond compare and notable for only one thing, it allowed Beethoven to starve [MS. Dowager Lady Leslie].

Earlier still, in 1906, Moore sent an intolerant letter to the American novelist Marquise Clara Lanza, who had just informed him of her conversion to the Catholic faith:

Your question regarding sacraments surprises me and it shows me that you have not understood – the passage [in *The Lake*] you wish explained is quite clear to those who are in a state of grace (my idea of grace is not yours) and everything depends on it. I will only tell you what Pascal says about sacraments – Sacraments help you to believe but they stupify you. I will venture to tell you that I regret that you have joined a religion from which the intelligence of the world has receded leaving a dry desert of dogma behind. The book you tell me you are writing is I suppose an account of your conversion, your admission into the home for lost dogs. Of course such homes should exist as there will always be lost dogs, but I don't look upon myself as one [MS. George S. MacManus Co.].

These outbursts are typical, as is the dialogue between Moore and his brother Maurice included in *Hail and Farewell*. Yet Moore himself was born of Catholic parents in predominantly Catholic Mayo. He was tutored by an Irish Catholic priest. He was sent to a Catholic school in England. In 1884 he proposed marriage to Maud O'Conor, his Catholic cousin. References to religion in his early correspondence and literature indicate that the evolution of his anti-Catholic attitudes was not sectarian. Rather (and curiously) it was a by-product of his development as a writer.

'To art ecclesiasticism is as deadly as arsenic is to the body', he warned Bernard Lopez, in a letter dated February 1877 and printed with *Martin Luther*. Responding to the threat of a Catholic censor, he confirmed that the play 'would not attack the fundamental doctrines of his religion, but only the abuses and vices which disgraced . . . the Church of Rome'. By the late 1870s Moore had fallen completely under the influence of the French naturalist writers, whose aim was to reinterpret life through art. Art 'should explain all things and embrace modern life in its entirety, in its endless ramifications, be . . . a new creed in a new civilization' (*Confessions of a Young Man*, Chapter 6).

The new creed became memorably evident in *A Drama in Muslin*. Writing to the Dutch author Frans Netscher in 1885, Moore explained

My new book deals with the questions: whether English [sic] girls . . . will take professions or continue to consider marriage as the only profession open to them. The scene is laid in Ireland during the land agitation – while the girls are crying for white dresses the peasants are crying for the soil . . . The principal character is an atheist who is likewise a virtuous woman [MS. Letterkundig Museum].

His intentions in creating the character of Alice Barton were further explained to an unidentified critic the following year:

I have attempted the supremely difficult task of using the realistic method as a means not of imposing vice but of exposing the mechanism of the virtuous mind. My heroine is an atheist: she is an atheist on the first page, she is an atheist on the last; she is neither prude nor prostitute but a woman endowed with much common sense and a deep rooted belief in the *practical rectitudes* of life . . . Judging by your notice of *A Mummer's Wife*, you seem interested in my work, and as no one has ever in fiction attempted to deal with the constructive side of unbelief I am tempted to call your attention to my aims in writing *A Drama in Muslin* [MS. Berg Collection].

Later in 1886, apparently defending himself against a charge of authorial intrusion, he wrote to Theodore Duret: 'Yes, I admit I side with Alice's unbelief in the latter part of the book but I cannot for a moment agree that in doing so I am overstepping the limits of the Balzac formula' [MS. Berg Collection]. Alice Barton's atheism was not exactly his, however, as a letter to his mother in 1887 indicates:

I have now taken up my abode I hope for good in Sussex . . . I am very fond of my friends and have entirely adopted their life – have said in fact thy people shall be my people, thy God shall be my God. I put on a high hat and take my umbrella and march to church every Sunday. I do not believe but I love Protestantism; if it is not the faith of my brain it is the faith of my heart. You will not I know feel much sympathy in these sentiments but you will agree with me that it is better to acquiesce in outward forms than to protest and so give scandal and offence [MS. National Library of Ireland].

Only a few weeks earlier, in letters to his publisher, Moore had been compelled to defend the manuscript *Confessions of a Young Man* from charges of blasphemy and a threat to abort publication. 'No one objects to anyone saying, "I don't believe" ', he informed his editor,

the only thing that can be taken objection to is *abuse*. You will see that I have cut out every abusive epithet; the passages as they now stand are mere statements. To take Christ as the socialist of the Galilee, using socialist as I clearly do in the sense of the God of pity, is not offensive; the rest is a bare statement of fact that the modern positivist, the socialist, denies Christ, therefore that Christ is lost and whelmed in the final triumph of Christianity. This is not orthodoxy but it is not blasphemy . . . Why I should not say that the new God, the God the positivists will create, will be dressed in broadcloth and wear a red necktie I cannot even conjecture – you struck out this passage [MS. National Library of Ireland].

The protests were heard again in 1906, when William Heinemann rejected Moore's recommendation of Edouard Dujardin's *La Source du Fleuve Chrétien*.

When you told me that you could not publish Dujardin's book I thought it was because your critic had found it stupid; apparently the only fault with it was that it was not reverent, orthodox, Anglican. I may be living in a dream but I thought all that kind of thing was at an end, and people published whatever they liked. Was Darwin orthodox? Has Herbert Spencer written in vain? [MS. William Heinemann Ltd.]

Heinemann's reservations apparently were not open for discussion. In 1915, having been informed of the subject of *The Brook Kerith*, he encouraged Moore to send the manuscript to another publisher.

Moore's letters reveal that he continued in 'outward forms' to act the part of a Protestant while inwardly he remained agnostic, but his attention became increasingly fixed on Roman Catholicism. He continued to correspond with Clara Lanza, and in 1888 collaborated with her in an attempt to turn her novel, *A Righteous Apostate* (1883), into a play.

The priest is the play as I see it. I should make him give up the priesthood because he cannot rid himself of love for Cordelia. Your treatment was a little tepid; mine would be more feverish. He can bear the priesthood no longer but will accept matrimony . . . Your priest must be a kind of Robert Elsmere. I speak of the new brotherhood, but you must invent another name [MS. George S. MacManus Co.].

The collaboration was not fruitful, but Moore made important use of Lanza's subject. The 'righteous apostate', dressed in broadcloth and a red necktie and called John Reid, was the leading protagonist in Moore's play *The Strike at Arlingford* (1893). The subject was returned to its Catholic setting in *The Lake*, in which a priest abandons the Church not simply for a woman, but for the humanity the woman represents.

The Lake might be viewed as the obverse of *Evelyn Innes* and *Sister Teresa*, companion novels in which the leading protagonist retreats from humanity to the Church. Moore began to mention *Evelyn Innes* in the early 1890s, while nearing the end of *Esther Waters*. In *The Musician* (29 September 1897) he attributed the subject to a true story about a French actress, told by the author Mary Robinson (later Duclaux). In 1894 he communicated with the editor W.T. Stead, who had been a friendly correspondent for several years:

I am considering a story the great part of which passes in a convent of cloistered nuns. I shall write this story if I can obtain certain necessary information regarding the discipline of such convents. I want very little, but the little I want is indispensable. I dare say everyone has his own way of working. I work from word of mouth description. I can describe a scene that has been related to me better than if I had witnessed it. So I should like to meet someone who had been in a convent, a professed nun would be best of all. That of course would be difficult to obtain, but one who had served her noviciate might [not] be. My nuns are Roman Catholic and I should like best a Roman Catholic, failing that anyone who had been in a convent of Anglican nuns would do, for the point of my story is not the discipline of any particular order but the entire question of a cloistered life. It was Mr. [H.W.] Massingham who suggested that I should write to you [MS. James D. Hart].

In a follow-up letter, Moore clarified his meaning in 'the entire question of a cloistered life': 'To live your life or to put your life aside, that is the question' [MS. James D. Hart]. Stead introduced Moore to Virginia Crawford. Ten years earlier Mrs. Crawford had been involved in one of the most shocking of Victorian divorce cases. In 1889, after becoming an assistant to Stead in his salvational causes, she was received into the Catholic Church by her friend Cardinal Manning. She was an ideal informant because she could draw from experiences of both the cloister and the demi-monde. Other helpers named in the correspondence included J-K Huysmans, whose *En Route* (1895) was much admired and partly imitated by Moore; Edward Martyn, the prototype for the

Catholic John Norton in *A Mere Accident*; Marie Agnes Beerbohm, Max's sister; and Angelena Frances Milman, a devout Anglican who was associated with the Community of the Resurrection. Lena Milman's fortune was bequeathed for the construction of the Church of Our Lady of Mercy and St. Thomas of Canterbury, in Gorton.

'I wonder if I shall be able to realize the full innocent life of nuns, some few of whom have renounced the world, others who have never known it', Moore wrote to Edmund Gosse in 1894. 'I don't know. I hope and am deeply interested' [MS. University of Leeds]. A year later he reported progress on the novel, then entitled *The Nun*, to Lady Eden. Lady Eden's husband, Sir William, was the model for Sir Owen Asher, one of Evelyn's lovers.

I am crazy about my novel. I think it will be better than *Esther*. I can imagine that poor nun reliving in memory all the past passion of her life, and in the solitude of her cell. I shall try to bring out more distinctly than it has ever been brought out something which neither Willy nor Lady Cunard understand very deeply, but which you I think can understand – I mean *la vie de couvent*. Those who know what that life is know how intense and penetrating it is, how sharp are its tears. Imagine my poor Evelyn recollecting the nights on board the boat, the sailors have got up a concert among themselves and Evelyn the most beautiful voice in Europe sings one night under the stars. How acute the memory of that song would be to her, more than when she sang in the opera houses, how sharpened her memory would be by the grey convent monotony – no more lovers, never another, never again would a man take her in his arms saying 'dearest'. How thin the Christ would grow on the wall, how far away, and how full and luminous would the grey Mediterranean nights seem, bewitched by memory. How wonderful is memory, memory is in literature what *clair obscure* is in painting. Writers make too little use of memory, recollection! How extraordinary is recollection . . . [MS. Sir John Eden, Bt.].

Moore was disappointed in the novel's reception. In general it was regarded as a trivial love story. But the critics who recognized his aims included Arthur Quiller-Couch (*The Speaker*), A.B. Walkley (*The Star*), Royal Cortisozz (*New York Daily Tribune*) and Ernst Heilborn (*Die Nation*). More than ten years earlier the atheist Alice Barton had explained that 'the ideal life should lie . . . in making the two ends meet – in making the ends of nature the ends also of what we call our conscience' (*A Drama in Muslin*, Book III, Chapter 1). Virginia Crawford, in a letter to the *Saturday Review* (18 June 1898) commenting on *Evelyn Innes*, unconsciously echoed this sentiment:

Mr. Moore's intention ... is to show that to a woman of Evelyn's temperament, brought up in Catholic traditions, the moral awakening was bound to come sooner or later, and that her conscience once roused could leave her no peace until she had brought her life once more into harmony with her inmost feelings, whatever the cost might be.

Moore complained about the lack of critical understanding in several letters, including one to Edmund Gosse in 1898:

Evelyn does not go back to virtue because she was brought up a Roman Catholic (I am incapable of such sectarian bigotry) but because it is her nature. We do not become mad we are born mad and Evelyn was born what she is. I showed the germ of the disease in the third chapter. Couch has an article in this week's *Speaker* which perfectly explains the idea, so the idea must have got on to the paper. Of course nothing is commoner than for a writer to fail to get his idea on to the paper but this cannot be my case since Couch states the idea formally. But all the other critics except you and he have understood little more than the external facts – a young girl with a beautiful voice elopes with a baronet, gets bitten by religion and repents. The book might have been written in Arabic for all they understood of it. But a young man on the stock exchange wrote, 'but you seem to make happiness impossible without belief'. Was it not clever of him to have understood so well? I dare say the book is not a very good book. Even so, that is no reason for seeing nothing but the surface. And truth to tell the reviewing has depressed me dreadfully. I have composed my epitaph: 'He discovered his own limitations and the limitless stupidity of the world' [MS. British Library].

In 1901, the year *Sister Teresa* was published, Moore began a ten-year residence in Dublin. His aim had been to contribute to the revival of Irish culture, but several factors, including lack of tolerance for the Catholic clergy, restricted his influence. He seemed to grow fond of baiting and attacking both laity and priests, as in this example from the *Irish Times* (28 October 1910), commenting on a clerical effort to rid Dublin of prostitutes:

It will seem strange to some that a clergyman of any denomination should write in so un-Christian a spirit, and this one could not have had the story of Christ and the woman of Samaria in his mind when he wrote the letter which you print to-day. Without having done twenty years' rescue work, Christ saw far deeper into the truth of the social evil than the clergyman. He knew that the evil had existed from the beginning, and what has been in the beginning will be till the end. And the moral of the story of the woman of Samaria is, that the little we may do to mitigate evil will be done by kindness, and not by persecution.

Moore's perception of Christ as an epitome of human goodness formed during the early 1900s and led him directly to the composition of *The Brook Kerith*, the novel he regarded as his finest literary achievement. Christ in *The Brook Kerith* survives the crucifixion and retires to a contemplative life at the monastery of the Essenes, the order in which He is said to have been educated. The idea of associating Christ with the Essenes probably derived from Thomas DeQuincey, whose essay on the subject Moore read and admired in the late 1880s. As an agnostic idealist, a pessimist convinced of the need for human aspiration, it was crucial for Moore to demystify Christ in order to make Him a divinity worthy of a modern, rational mind. Yet it was necessary, in light of Moore's aesthetic views, to compose a portrait of Christ that conformed with the primary sources: the synoptic Gospels. Moore's acknowledgment of the problem is reflected in several letters, including one to William Heinemann written soon after Moore's journey to Palestine in 1914:

One thing perplexes me: Jesus never said He was God, I could show a dozen texts that prove He was looked upon as a prophet – greater than the other prophets if you will but no more. In the Acts His relation to the Father is clearly stated. But what strikes me more than the text is the fact that no Jew could entertain the thought of a second God; such a thought was unthinkable in the 1st century. That the Christian began to play with the idea of the man-god in the Gospels is true enough but Christ's divinity had begun to separate itself from Judaism when the Gospels were written. I'd give something for a text showing that Jesus said He was God. My story is therefore weakest at the point at which it will occur to no one to question it. [MS. William Heinemann Ltd.]

While the novel was still in manuscript, Moore sent portions to the Irish author Susan Mitchell, who was preparing a study of Moore. Her comments on the text disappointed him, for she apparently failed to understand that the new Christ was not a defamation of the old. His frustration was indicated in a letter to George Russell in 1916, a few weeks before *The Brook Kerith* was published:

The phrase 'breaking up the mould' is not very clear to me. First of all, there is no mould. Jesus is a legendary figure, illusive and illusory, and not an historical figure, incoherent and contradictory: a compilation from various sources like all legendary characters. Out of this chaos I have tried to create a human being and the question at issue is: have I succeeded in creating a human being out of this chaos? I'd understand the phrase 'breaking up the mould' better if it had been applied to St. Paul [MS. Ulrich Middeldorf].

Following publication of the novel, Moore's final word on the subject was addressed to the *Pall Mall Gazette* (4 September 1916):

You write:'Following a fairly common practice,the author discredits the Resurrection and endows Jesus with a further term of mortal life, during which Jesus renounces all pretentions of divinity and embraces a sort of lachrymose pantheism.'

But Jesus does not lay claim to divinity in *The Brook Kerith*. He merely tries to convince Himself that He is the Messiah promised to the Jews, and I thought I had made this very important point quite clear, and that everybody would see that I was following certain well-known texts in Matthew and Mark, texts in which Jesus repudiates any comparison between Him and the Father. The prelates have tried to explain away these texts, but they have not succeeded in doing so to the satisfaction of many people. The Arians, who pointed to the text 'Why do you call me good, none is good but God', which they said was enforced by texts from St. Paul's Epistles, were persecuted by the so-called Orthodox Church about the year 385, and the so-called Arian heresy has lasted into the present day under the name of Unitarianism. Many very intelligent and respectable people have belonged to this sect and have looked upon themselves as Christians, John Milton, among others of less poetical celebrity, but not less religious fervour.

It has always seemed to a great number of people that the claim to the divinity of Jesus did not begin to emerge until the Gospel of John was published about the middle of the second century, nearly a hundred years after the death of Jesus. This Gospel is looked upon by all critics, Agnostic, Protestant, and Roman Catholic, as an ecclesiastical work of no historical value. It contains scenes at which the author was not present and could not have had any knowledge of, notably the scene in which Pilate calls Jesus into the Praetorium and talks with Him alone. The Evangelist supplies Pilate and Jesus with some admirable dialogue, plausible enough, but which must have come out of the Evangelist's imagination in the same way as many scenes in *The Brook Kerith* came out of mine. In writing *The Brook Kerith* I have followed the example of the Evangelist by including scenes at which I was certainly not present, and if I have done this on a larger scale than John I may still plead that it was he who set the example.

THE LOVER

Writing to Lord Howard de Walden in 1905 about Richard Wagner's Mathilde, Moore remarked that 'she was one of the great – a word is wanting – lovers of the world, different from Héloise, St. Teresa or the Portuguese nun' (MS. Lord Howard de Walden). The strange assortment of lovers *cum* holy women is characteristic of aspects of his literature. In life he was rather less attentive to spiritual attributes and explained, sometimes to the discomfort of his auditors, that his favourite experience of women was carnal. 'The human soul is what is most interesting in literature, I might even add in love,' he told Clara Lanza in 1890; 'we cannot go to bed with souls it is true, but – well, a soul and a good figure go far to make the hours less harsh' (MS. University of Washington).

Just as Moore was preoccupied by religion without enjoying the advantage of belief in God, he was devoted to women without ever having married or achieved an entirely felicitous love affair. The loss of his virginity, fictionalized in the fourth chapter of *Vale* (1914), may be dated to early 1874. The incident of *la belle Hollandais* is associated with a masked ball to which he alluded in a letter to his mother. Three years later he met an Irish heiress in Paris and endeavoured to propose marriage. Writing to his mother of his hopes, he remarked:

What a great truth it is [that] a virtuous woman is a woman who does not compromise herself. I have had often and often certain and the most certain of all proofs that I have not been disliked by women. It will certainly annoy me if I cannot make this dowered little girl like me. I suppose it will be like my luck. Being liked by a Princess or a Marquise brings little or nothing (if an honest man). I feel I won't succeed but we will see [MS. National Library of Ireland].

(His marriage plans collapsed when he learned that the girl's fortune did not meet his expectations.)

In 1879 he again confided to his mother that he was trying to seduce an aristocrat, the wife of the composer Marquis d'Osmond. His efforts were interrupted by reduced receipts from Moore Hall which forced his departure from France. Five years passed before another romantic attachment was recorded, this time with an Irish cousin. It appears that he was in love and proposed marriage, but was foiled by the girl's disapproving parents.

Writing to his brother Maurice in 1888, Moore reported:

My life is given up more than ever to art, I turned aside from marriage and am getting rid of my mistress. I am now in the plenitude of artistic life and I live in the giddiness, the madness, the exultation of an unceasing creation [MS. National Library of Ireland].

The mistress is unidentified, but was probably the recipient of a letter written later the same year:

Moore Hall, Co. Mayo, in the early 1900s. George Moore's ancestral home, it was burned during the Civil War, in 1923.

'Le Dandy des Batignolles' (a Parisian nickname), George Moore c.1879. A pencil and black chalk sketch originally attributed to Edgar Degas. Courtesy of the Ashmolean Museum, Oxford.

Photograph of Moore, c.1887, in Shoreham where he was working on *Confessions of a Young Man*. Although only first published in *The Sketch* on 30 August 1893, this picture was taken at that time.

George Moore aged 35, in 1887, by Jacques Emile Blanche. Courtesy of the Musées de Rouen.

George Moore in 1896, by William Rothenstein. Courtesy the National Gallery of Ireland. This pencil drawing was commissioned by the publisher Walter Scott for the frontispiece of the second edition of *Modern Painting* (1896). It was rejected in favour of a portrait by Edouard Manet.

Within the illustration:
ONE HALF-PENNY NET

BELTAINE

An Occasional Publication.   Number Three.   *April* 1900.

THE ORGAN OF THE IRISH LITERARY THEATRE

EDITED BY W. B. YEATS · · · ·

LONDON : AT THE SIGN OF THE UNICORN.

In The graceful
Year 1900
George Moore
& Victoria
Returned
To Ireland

LADY FINGALL
DROPS
Edward Martyn

W. B. Y
plays the
organ —

'In the graceful year 1900 George Moore & Victoria returned to Ireland', by Jack B. Yeats. Courtesy of Michael B. Yeats and Anne Yeats, and the Henry W. and Albert A. Berg Collection of the New York Public Library, Astor, Lenox and Tilden Foundations.

Moore travelled to Dublin in February 1900 for a performance of *The Bending of the Bough*. To celebrate the success of the Irish Literary Theatre productions there was a luncheon at the Gresham Hotel on 22 February for its members. Responding to a toast offered by Douglas Hyde, Moore so impressed the gathering that the *Freeman's Journal* reported: 'Mr. George Moore's speech on the occasion was, in a sense, more important than the occasion itself'.

The following month he sent an inflammatory letter to the *United*

George Moore in 1905, by John Butler Yeats. Courtesy of Michael B. Yeats and Anne Yeats, and the National Gallery of Ireland. Commissioned by John Quinn for his New York apartment. Started in August 1905, it was never finished, but Quinn accepted it, aware that the likeness could not be bettered.

Irishman, condemning Queen Victoria's plans to visit Ireland. The letter apparently offset the good impression he had made. The Queen went ahead with her visit, but according to the Dublin *Daily Express* of 19 January 1901, Moore's letter cost him membership of the Irish Literary Society.

Left: Cartoon of George Moore, probably by Robert Gregory, from one of Lady Gregory's albums. Courtesy of Mrs. R.G. Gregory *Below:* A caricature of George Moore being painted by Miss S.C. Harrison; from a letter by Sir William Orpen. Courtesy of the National Library of Ireland.

George Moore, aged 55, in 1907 by Miss Sara Celia Harrison. Courtesy of the Humanities Research Center, University of Texas at Austin.

'G Moore giving his memorial lecture at the RHA' in 1904, by John Butler Yeats. Courtesy of Michael B. Yeats and Anne Yeats, and the Henry W. and Albert A. Berg Collection of the New York Public Library, Astor, Lenox and Tilden Foundations.

'An illustration for "Hail and Farewell"': Mr. Moore under the influence of the Boer War', a cartoon by Max Beerbohm, dated 1911. Courtesy of Mrs. Eva Reichmann, and the Ashmolean Museum, Oxford. Moore's comforters are (l. to r.) P. Wilson Steer, Walter Sickert and Henry Tonks.

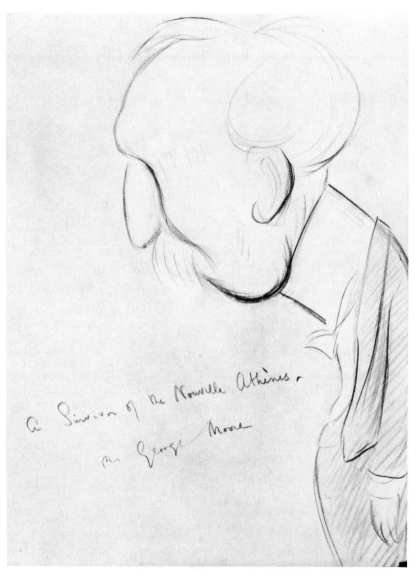

'A survivor of the Nouvelle Athènes, Mr. George Moore', a caricature
drawn by Max Beerbohm, Courtesy of Mrs. Eva Reichmann. The picture is
now in the Humanities Research Center, University of Texas at Austin.

'Saturday night in The Vale' by Henry Tonks, 1929. Courtesy of the Tate Gallery, London. Moore, who described himself in this painting as 'a flabby old cook', reads from the manuscript of *Aphrodite in Aulis*. In the background from l. to r. are St. John Hutchinson, Philip Wilson Steer, Henry Tonks, and Mary Hutchinson. The painting was commissioned by Sir William Orpen.

Above: George Moore returning from a shoot in the grounds of Coole Park, with Tonks. *Below*: George Moore, Edouard Dujardin and unidentified ladies at Le Val Changis. Courtesy of Robert Becker. Moore was a frequent visitor to Dujardin's home near Fontainbleau. Over the garden gate there is a plaque reading: 'Adieu Val! Adieu à jamais! / Forêt, pelouse et la terrace / Où j'ai vu groupé tout Parnasse / Pendant vingt ans au mois de mai / George MOORE'.

A sketch of George Moore by Sir William Orpen. Courtesy of the Knight of Glin.

George Moore in February 1932, by Francis Dodd. Courtesy of the National Portrait Gallery, London.

What you thought of my letter, whether it made you laugh or cry, whether you burnt it or preserved it matters to me not at all, but I am sorry you failed to understand it. There is no use going into details, suffice it to say that latterly your society has become to me quite unbearable; I write this so that you may not think it surprising if I do not come to see you when I am in London. We have been very intimate, this intimacy must cease, that is all. You cannot remember who you are, you cannot remember who I am, so for the future when we meet we must meet as acquaintances not as friends. I do not care unless you do to press this matter any further [MS. Gordon N. Ray].

Despite the appearance of putting aside his relations with women, it seems that Moore began a love affair at about this time with the author Ada Leverson. Before emotions subsided into a calm friendship, Moore asked Mrs. Leverson to obtain a divorce from her husband and marry him. Her letters to Moore survive in the custody of her grandson. Soon after, in the late 1880s, Moore returned to London after residing two years in Sussex. His friend Sir William Nevill Geary introduced him to the critic and translator Lena Milman. The friendship which followed was later described by Geary as one of the two 'serious love affairs' in Moore's life (letter to Joseph Hone, MS. University of Washington). By 'serious' he meant to suggest hopes of matrimony. Miss Milman was married in 1908 to a civil servant. The other 'serious' affair of the early 1890s was with the author Pearl Craigie, who likewise declined to marry. Most of Moore's letters to Mrs. Craigie have not come to light; nor have the letters he wrote to the painter Clara Christian, who became his mistress in the later 1890s and continued the intimacy for several years.

It is not likely that the letters, if they do become available, will contain vividly passionate appeals. Moore confessed to Clara Lanza in 1891:

The few ladies who have – well, been kind to me, have always insisted on my writing to them 'Dear Mrs. ——, Thanks very much for your kind invitation which I accept with much pleasure'. A love affair conducted on these heartless lines is somewhat chilling. Such has been my fate and to you and to you only have I ever written anything but stereotyped phrases [MS. Berg Collection].

Moore's confession is apparently true. It is fortunate therefore that the Marquise Clara Lanza preserved all his letters and that most have been located. They show his affection for women, the style of his lovemaking, and the meaning he attached to it.

By far, the most important love affair of Moore's life was with Lady Cunard. Maud Alice Burke, the daughter of a California gold mine proprietor, was born on 31 August 1876 (not 1872, as reported elsewhere). During her childhood her father died and her mother remarried, but her stepfather's household in New York was apparently unsuitable for the young girl. She was informally adopted by General Horace W. Carpentier (Ret.), a wealthy banker who had been associated with Maud's father during the Gold Rush. Maud was at least partly educated in Europe. There and in America she was perceived as Carpentier's heiress: thus she commanded considerable attention in the marriage market.

Apparently Moore met Maud Burke in France in September 1893 (a year earlier than reported elsewhere) while he was a guest in the home of the painter Jacques-Émile Blanche, in Auteuil. The experience was mentioned in a letter to Maurice Moore:

I nearly died of seasickness coming over from France. I had a most delicious love adventure there. Generally my loves are mature but this one is a young girl of 18 – I think the most beautiful girl I ever saw in my life. Beauty generally doesn't fetch me but this one did. What she could see in me to rave about I cannot think. I have been wondering ever since, a *blasé roué* like me, rotten with literature and art to which Wagnerism has lately been added . . . My golden-haired siren is an heiress; she wanted me to marry her but I said that that would be dishonourable, that I never went after a girl for her money. Only five days but when the lady is amorous and the aunt is complacent or witless a good deal can be done. *'J'ai rêvé dans la grotte où nage la sirène'*. That women may lose their virtue certainly makes life worth living [MS. National Library of Ireland].

Maude Burke returned to America. Following a slightly scandalous engagement to Prince André Poniatowski and another visit to Europe, she married Sir Bache Cunard, Bt., in New York. He occasionally resided at his mother's property there. The marriage was loveless but not childless: a daughter was born in March 1896. Evidence in Moore's letters to his brother Maurice and to the Edens suggests that Moore was Nancy Cunard's father. In 1922 Jacques-Émile Blanche informed Barrett H. Clark that Moore believed he was.

The significance of his letters to Lady Cunard was stressed by Moore during his life. When he appointed Charles Morgan as his official biographer, he ranked the letters as 'the most valuable existing source, outside his own memory and his autobiographical writings' (Charles Morgan, *Epitaph on George Moore*, 1935, p. 3). He insisted that without the letters a definitive biography would be impossible. After Moore's death, Lady Cunard refused to allow Morgan to examine the correspondence and he, following his promise to Moore, withdrew from the project.

'Many more' than a thousand letters were preserved by Lady Cunard, at least until the 1930s. By the terms of her will, they became the property of Sir Sacheverell Sitwell. For unknown reasons, four years elapsed between Lady Cunard's death in 1948 and the transfer of the correspondence by her executor, Mr. Loel Guinness. When Sitwell did receive the bequest, only 282 letters were contained in it. Most of these were published by Sir Rupert Hart-Davis in 1957.

Lady Cunard's desire for privacy may have provoked her to destroy the bulk of the correspondence, but she never mentioned having done so. On the contrary, in the 1940s when Sir Shane Leslie communicated his wish to examine them, she replied: 'It was sweet of you to write about GM's letters but alas I can't show them to you as they are now in a bank far away'. . . (MS. Robert S. Becker). She was not referring to the 282 letters transferred to Sitwell, for these were in her possession and were shown at about this time to Mr. Peter Quennell.

It is fair to speculate that the bulk of the letters was preserved in a safe-deposit box in America, where Lady Cunard had moved in 1939 with the intention of remaining indefinitely. Eventually they may come to light. Two letters recently have been located, one in the University of San Francisco Library, the other, reprinted below, now in the present writer's collection.

Feb 14th 1898   92 Victoria Street
I send you the proofs – I fancy that they are about a third of the book. I am feeling so depressed that I cannot come to tea; you would only think me hateful. Do you know what a black melancholy is? If there was only a reason but it is the sorrow of life, the primal sorrow. This sounds melodramatic, exaggerated, pedantic. Indifferent as the fiction doubtless is it is better than the horrible reality known as

George Moore

[MS. Robert S. Becker]

It is pleasant to wonder when and where others will appear.

GEORGE MOORE'S MEDIEVALISM: A MODERN TRIPTYCH

GARETH W. DUNLEAVY

I first read George Moore's *Héloïse and Abélard* and James Stephens *The Crock of Gold* three decades ago at the bidding of a noted medievalist, John Spargo. His prediction that *Héloïse and Abélard* would evoke for me the renaissance of twelfth-century France proved true. Moore's book also confirmed remarks made about Heloise and Abelard by Henry Adams: with all its sparkle, the twelfth century would have been more remote without that couple. Indeed, when Moore called his book 'modern both in spirit and mood,' he was his own best critic. *The Crock of Gold* introduced me to another part of the medieval forest, Celtic (mainly Irish) myth and legend. Although, astonishingly, Celtic tradition is *terra incognita* to many medievalists and modernists, in it certain well-known twentieth-century poets and dreamers have found inspiration for some of their most significant work. The evidence that Moore was among those who borrowed, reworked, and 'remoulded' (his word) material from medieval sources, both continental and insular, is strongest in three of his later works.[1]

In the short stories of *A Story-Teller's Holiday* (1918), George Moore drew heavily on the anthology of Old Irish monastic and secular poetry and the lives and legends of Irish saints that had become available to readers of English in the nineteenth century. In *Héloïse and Abélard* (1921) he turned to France for his story of the conflicts of 'the cathedral of the thousand arches', the courts of love, and the cult of permissive adultery celebrated in troubadour lyrics. In *Ulick and Soracha* (1926) he grafted the remnants of the fast-fading continental world of castles, crusades, and courtly love on to fourteenth-century Ireland, deep in the throes of the Bruce invasion and savage civil factionalism. Amid this murderous strife Moore returned Ulick de Burgo, *émigré* Irish trouvère and bastard son of the great Red Earl, Richard de Burgo, to Ireland, ostensibly to help his father repulse Edward Bruce, but actually to snatch from her nunnery a compliant Irish princess, daughter of his father's ally.

Moore's preparation for the writing of his three major 'medieval' books was thorough and wide-ranging: he drew from his own reading, from extensive travel, and from carefully cultivated associations with historians, philologists, philosophers, and friends who were enthusiastic students of the medieval scene. In the rearrangement and remoulding of his material, Moore telescoped chronology, cut and spliced eras and events, expanded or invented both imaginatively and mischievously on the basis of a clue or suggestion in his sources.[2] For Moore, the thrill of the hunt lay not in recording the killing of kings but in tracking the unicorn of artistic truth. The effect on readers familiar with his medieval sources at first may be disconcerting, somewhat like trying to collate the Irish *Annals of the Four Masters*, held in one hand, with the Duc de Berri's *Book of Hours* held in the other. Moore, however, may have brought off the near impossible merger or integration, not of the facts of 'objective history' lying in disparate and remote cells in twelfth-century France and eighth- through fourteenth-century Ireland, but of three artistic themes, popular in medieval literature and selected by him because of their special significance for twentieth-century Ireland. What Moore created, in other words, was not the *speculum* or mirror of medieval iconography but the triptych. In its three panels are presented, first, 'The Ruin of Ireland' (an elegy with apocalyptic undertones); second, the antithetical medieval imagery of 'Friendly Forest' and 'Fearsome Wood' (the former, a nearly pastoral romantic refuge or liberating landscape, the latter, a savage, predatory, alien place); third, another antithesis, the ascetic, self-denying, spiritual love of the monastery cell and the erotic, self-indulgent, profane love of the castle bedchamber.

'THE RUIN OF IRELAND'

The first panel of Moore's triptych, 'The Ruin of Ireland', is filled with elegiac scenes bordering on the apocalyptic. The spur to Moore's imagination here is not the *ubi sunt* theme of classical or Germanic literature but the native theme of ruin found in *Selections from Ancient Irish Poetry* (1911) by Kuno Meyer, one of the leading Celticists of his time.[3] Meyer's translations of early Irish monastic and secular poetry were a chief source for Moore's borrowing and remoulding in *A Story-Teller's Holiday* and *Ulick and Soracha*. For example, Moore had read Meyer's translation of 'The Fort of Rathangan' (*Selections*, p. 93):

> The fort over against the oak-wood,
> Once it was Bruidge's, it was Cathal's,

It was Aed's, it was Ailill's,
It was Conaing's, it was Cuiline's,
It was Maelduin's:
The fort remains after each in his turn –
And the kings asleep in the ground.

The transience of royal glory, the frailty of human life, whether of prince or cottager, is the note repeated in two poems that follow: 'The Deserted Home' and 'Alexander the Great'. To invoke, as has one critic, 'the disembodied melancholy of the Celtic twilight' as the agent that 'profoundly affected Moore's imagination' in his medieval books does a disservice both to Moore and to his early Irish sources.[4] Less vague and more plausible is the evidence that links the dominant 'Ruin of Ireland' theme in the first panel of Moore's triptych with Moore's reading of Meyer's translations of these poems.

Setting forth on what becomes a circular journey from London's Euston Station to the wilds of Mayo and return, Moore's narrator in *A Story-Teller's Holiday* settles back to contemplate the panorama, the sharp contrast between English and Irish landscapes – one 'deliberately wooded', the other of a 'wild and uncouth nature'. 'Then you're going to Ireland to see the ruins?' asks another traveller with whom he has a casual conversation. 'It was for its ruins that we all loved Ireland,' asserts the narrator in reply (p. 7). Later, viewing the destruction in Dublin left by the 1916 Rising, the 'empty shells' of the Imperial Hotel and the General Post Office, the narrator remarks the 'phantoms' of 'a city that has passed away,' 'shapeless mounds' where the Henry Street cats, reminiscent of men who 'twenty thousand years before Pompeii' groped amid incomprehensible earthquakes, seek their shattered hearths (pp. 9, 11). Before he leaves for the west the narrator hears that Yeats has taken up residence in a ruined castle in Galway and is 'weaving the myths that will preserve his works when all life has departed from them' (p. 12). As the train moves westward, the ruined lock house of a ruined canal catches his eye, and he muses, 'In Ireland nothing disappears, all is that ever was . . .' (p. 20), whether the fort of chieftains at Rathangan or cabins, castles, and canals. Some hours later, at last in the vicinity of the Big House he knows best, the seat of Sir Hugh of Muchloon (Muckloon is the local name for the hill near Partry on which Moore Hall was built[5]), the narrator learns that it now stands empty – and that after the departure of its present owner, Muchloon will be added to the list of ruins that encumber Ireland. 'The finest assortment of ruins the world can show. From the fifth century onwards every century is represented; English and

Irish ruins, ruined houses and ruined lives,' declares the narrator's gloomy fellow traveller.

Following this introduction, elegiac focus in *The Story-Teller's Holiday* shifts between panoramic and personal. It is the personal note, for example, that is sounded in Moore's adaptation of the story of two poets, Liadin and Curither, from Meyer's translation (*Selections*, pp. 65–66). In the dialogue between Liadin and her lover, Curither, on the one hand, and the cleric Cummins Mac Fiachna on the other, the hermit speaks of a 'simple truth': 'Our possessions and our health pass away from us; all things pass away from us except one thing only, . . . the love of God' (pp. 87–88). The personal reminder, signified by a ruin, is present again in the story of Marban, the monk who breaks his vows and falls desperately in love with Luachet, the ravishing young novice. A ruined fort is the site chosen by the lovers for their one rapturous night as they make their escape. Alec Trusselby's bizarre story of St. Moling and Sister Ligach is set in a convent that now is an 'ivied ruin', 'little more than a heap of stones' with 'traces of ancient walls that the earth had not yet overgrown' (p. 174). At the conclusion of *A Story-Teller's Holiday* Muchloon is once more linked with the ancient Irish world through ruined forts and castles and dead kings. In the final panoramic scene of the triptych, it overlooks Lough Carra. Visible on the shores of the lake are the derelict castle and burned and abandoned cottages. Together they stand, all these ruins: the home of the chieftains; the home of descendants of the chieftains who became masters of the Big House; the homes of the chieftains' vassals who became the Big House tenants. Muchloon has taken its place among them; it has become 'a relic, a ruin, a corpse' (p. 348). For although the owner cannot give the order for the lead to be torn from its roof, he will never return to it. One of a thousand eighteenth-century houses in Ireland, it is forever linked to the past, to ancient Ireland and beyond – to the biblical Nineveh that passed from memory so rapidly that 'the shepherds who fed their flocks among the ruins could not tell Xenephon the name of the bygone city' (p. 353).

In *Ulick and Soracha*, a historical romance played against the background of the fierce Bruce wars of fourteenth-century Ireland, destruction and violence again evoke the 'Ruin of Ireland' panel of Moore's triptych. In this work, for his recreation of a saga of devastation of castle and cottage and the fall of Gaelic chieftains, Moore was indebted to Edmund Curtis's *History of Medieval Ireland* (1923).[6] In addition to his fascination with the events recounted by Curtis, Moore was struck by the author's terse and vivid style. The invasion of Ireland by Robert Bruce's brother Edward in May, 1315; the slowness of England's Edward II to move against the Scottish invaders; the ill-fated effort of the Gaelic confederacy under young Felim O'Conor to overthrow the Anglo-Normans at the Battle of Athenry in August, 1316; the collapse of Bruce's dream of a Celtic hegemony – all fascinated Moore. For him, the death of O'Conor and scores of his Irish chieftains at Athenry and the demise in 1318 of Edward Bruce with three thousand Scottish and Irish allies at his side supplied an apocalyptic background for his novel.

Ironically, in *Ulick and Soracha*, the toll of death and destruction at the most decisive time in Ireland's history since the coming of Strongbow means little to Sir Ulick de Burgo, Moore's chief character. The illegitimate son of the Great Earl, Richard de Burgo, engages in hot pursuit not of the enemies of his father but the body of the Princess Soracha. Not until Ulick looks on the deserted house of his mother in Ballinrobe and hears repeated his father the Earl's pronouncement that the house will stand 'with nothing taken from it and nothing put into it, till everything crumbles into the dust out of which all things come and into which all things will go' (p. 81) does the Ruin of Ireland theme penetrate Ulick's consciousness. In the middle of his serio-comic quest to abduct the Princess Soracha, Ulick turns to his harper, Tadgh O Doracha, to observe: 'A desolate country . . . unending wars and forays, murders, burnings, destruction, hard meat everywhere despite the splendid herds that stand knee-deep in succulent herbage' (p. 107).

The most striking instance of Moore's reinforcement from Old Irish sources of the 'Ruin of Ireland' theme in *Ulick and Soracha* is his introduction of the *Caillech Berri*, 'The Old Woman of Beare'. Moore took this legendary provincial goddess – mother of races and builder of cairns – directly from Meyer's *Selections*.[7] Known in *Ulick and Soracha* as Ann Gregan, 'The Old Woman of Athlone', she is Moore's fourteenth-century reincarnation of the ancient woman of the ninth-century poem. Summoned to heal the wounds inflicted on Tadgh by his master, Ann Gregan becomes Mother Ireland in Moore's hands. This filthy, ill-clad, outcast, a former mistress of the conqueror's governor of Athlone, is the personification of the 'Ruin of Ireland' theme in a passage based directly on Meyer's translation: 'The old woman of Beare, Tadhg, tells that time when she wore a new smock every day and that her arms were once wound around kings . . . The old Irish poem awakens sight of Ann Gregan, and I see her in my thoughts watching a herd of swine under these oaks, saying to herself: every acorn has to drop, and I, that had fine days and nights with kings, drinking mead and wine by the light of shining candles, today drink whey water when I can get it, among shrivelled old hags. I see upon my cloak long grey hairs, and the curled patch of my body is grey too. The flood wave and the second ebb-tide have all come to me. I am the Old Woman of Athlone. The flood wave will not reach the silence of my kitchen; my companions of old time are all laid in darkness. O happy isle of the great sea which the flood reaches after the ebb! But I do not expect flood after ebb to come to me. There is scarce a little place to-day that I can recognize; all is on the ebb!' (p. 119). Moore has followed the early medieval source in Meyer's translation nearly word-for-word, inserting them to heighten the elegiac motif of *Ulick and Soracha*.

In *Héloïse and Abélard*, Moore invented a scene from Arthurian legend to prefigure the collapse of Celtic hegemony that takes place during the Bruce war in fourteenth-century Ireland. In the novel Jean Guiscard tells Abelard of how he retreats to a forest cave to rouse his lady to forgiveness and of how he is led by deer and wolves to a dilapidated hall in the forest where he found Arthur, 'the once and future king', with his court and sword and a trumpet lying on a table before them. When Guiscard takes up the sword and blows the trumpet, king, court and ruined castle all vanish (II, p. 22).[8]

'THE FRIENDLY FOREST' AND 'THE FEARSOME WOOD'

The second panel of Moore's modern triptych exploits the medieval antithesis between what can be called 'the friendly forest' and 'the fearsome wood'. Examples of 'the friendly forest' are found in the thirteenth-century *Roman de la Rose* written by Guillaume de Lorris and Jean de Meung and in Chaucer's *Book of the Duchess*.[9] 'The fearsome wood' is reflected in Gawain's journey through the 'wild terrene' in *Sir Gawain and the Green Knight*; in scenes from Malory's *Morte Darthur*, after Lancelot has bolted to the woods to follow the life of the hermit; and in the *Cat Coit Celidon*, where the Welsh Myrddin wanders mad for fifty years. 'The friendly forest' of medieval literature was a surrogate Eden that offered not just sanctuary and a sense of solidarity with nature but often the means of subsistence: fish, game, fowl, berries, and nuts. 'The fearsome wood', on the other hand, was dark and hostile to travellers: cold, with showers of sleet and rain, close to impenetrable in its roughness; the haunt of wolves, boars, brigands, and madmen.

Out of the 'friendly forest' often came the sacred (and knighted!) fool. In Moore's *Peronnik the Fool* (1921), an expansion of a medieval romance he had barely touched on in *Héloïse and*

Abélard, the hero is a half-wit resident of the friendly forest who strays from it only to prove that he can become a pure knight. He is on intimate terms with the forest, knowing it as no one else knows it, and is 'happy in the enchantment of the forest, and at home in it even as the birds and animals' (p. 142). Moore's 'innocent fool of the forest' is reminiscent of Chaucer's Sir Thopas, the innocent effeminate knight who 'priketh thrugh a fair forest' in the mock riming romance of the *Canterbury Tales*.

It is from the 'friendly forest' of medieval Irish poetry that Moore took also the character of Suibhne Geilt, 'mad Sweeney', whom he then made into Alec Trusselby, the twentieth-century Westport seanachie who recited the tales of *A Story-Teller's Holiday*. In Old and Middle Irish tradition, Suibhne is a guilt-ridden Irish prince who went mad at the Battle of Mag Rath in the north of Ireland in A.D. 639 and afterwards took to the forest, living far from the society of men and women. Alec, the fern-gathering seanachie who first reminded the narrator of a Jesus figure out of a fifteenth-century Fra Angelico painting and then 'Christina Rossetti in a blonde beard', took on in Moore's imagination the identity of Sweeney. Like Sweeney, Alec had reputedly built a summer house in a great tree and was reported to sometimes break into speech like a bird's call (p. 64). In the twelfth-century version of *Buile Suibhne* the mad prince referred to himself as being 'alone in an ivied tree-top'.[10] The ancient Irish Sweeney had lost his reason from the strain of battle; Alec Trusselby had suffered sunstroke in America, and since his return to Ireland spends his summers in the forest where he collects ferns for sale to the townspeople. Though slightly odd, he is respected for his story-telling ability and is invited to spend winters with various families as their resident seanachie. Like the mad Sweeney of the forest, Alec Trusselby had 'caught his style from the moody blackbird' and 'the meditative thrush' (p. 64). In *Ulick and Soracha* Moore reintroduces the figure of mad Sweeney, this time as the hermit whom Tadgh and Ulick meet in the friendly forest of Glen Bolcane. It boasts water sweeter than the wines of France and is filled with the melodious calls of blackbird, thrush, and grey lark. Tadgh and Ulick linger there to enjoy the nuts and fruit harvested by the hermit (p. 125).

Moore's fourteenth-century Glen Bolcane of *Ulick and Soracha* is actually Glenn Bolcáin of the ninth-century poem 'Suibne in the Woods', in which the mad Irish prince of the friendly Irish medieval forest proclaims: 'Glenn mBolcáin is my permanent abode/ truly have I made it my own; many nights have I practised vigorous/ running to the mountain peak'.[11] In Glenn Bolcáin Suibhne had found a permanent refuge: 'Good is its pure blue water; good its clean fierce wind; good its cress-green water cress . . .'[12] More than any other place, Glenn Bolcáin is where Suibhne would 'prefer the site of a single hut'. The mad hermit of *Ulick and Soracha* describes to Ulick and Tadgh how he has rushed out between the opposing sides in a battle to propose costumes of silk for his lord's people. Jeered and cursed by both sides, he has fled the field and crossed to Britain where he has met another madman with whom he shares the fruits of the friendly forest until the day of his return to Ireland. To Ulick and Tadgh he predicts that he will meet death at the end of a cow's horn. It is Suibne of the early Irish poem who foresees his death 'by the instrumentality of an antler-peak'.[13]

In a 1926 interview with Austin Clarke, Moore called the Sweeney legend 'one of the great stories of the world . . .' 'And yet,' he asks, 'how many know of its existence?' For Moore nature was never 'so near, so wild, so tender' as in the Old Irish tales and poems about Suibhne, and he told Clarke that the story had 'inspired half my own book and none of the critics noticed the fact'.[14]

In the tale of Liadin and Cuirithir, which Moore had reshaped from Meyer's translation for *A Story-Teller's Holiday*, the poet and her lover find sanctuary on the hermit Cummins's wooded island, while close by they can see the fearsome wood 'that had a bad name for wolves' (p. 86). In Cummins's friendly forest of rowan, ash, and beech trees, the two lovers can only gaze at one another, but they are safe from harm. The peace and tranquility of the forest are exemplified in a passage in which Moore shows the monk illuminating a manuscript in his forest cell: 'and while I am at work, weaving garlands and finding nooks and corners for the birds and the weasels and the squirrels and badgers and the foxes of my little domain, my cat will be watching for mice as patient as myself' (p. 90). The monk of the Old Irish poem, 'Pangur Ban', is a grammarian rather than an illuminator, but the theme of solidarity of man with nature is the same in the medieval original and in Moore's adaptation.

In 'King and Hermit', another early Irish poem translated by Meyer, Marban, brother of a seventh-century king of Connacht, had renounced the life of the warrior-prince for that of a hermit. His brother comes to Marban to persuade him to return to the court, but in a catalogue of more than twenty stanzas Marban recounts the delights of his life in the friendly forest so convincingly that the king declares his readiness to leave his kingdom and join his brother.[15] It is to Marban's forest that Tadgh and his master retire at the end of *Ulick and Soracha*. For Tadgh as he walked there, 'the island seemed to grow bigger, opening out in every direction, with sinuous paths leading round tall groups of trees, elms seeking the sky and not finding it till they had overgrown the crowding beeches' (p. 199). With its primroses, dog violets, cowslips, and profusion of birches and larch, Moore's fourteenth-century version of Marban's forest is as attractive as its original in the Old Irish poem. Moore's narrator evokes the full lush beauty of that friendly forest described in 'King and Hermit' by quoting, virtually unchanged, the final stanza of Meyer's translation: 'I would give my glorious kingship, with the share of my father's heritage – To the hour of my death I would forfeit it to be in thy company, O Marban' (p. 200).[16] Moore gives his readers a last glimpse of Marban's demi-Eden when Biddy strips to give her husband Tadgh a deathbed view of a woman's beauty: 'Is there a finer place for a woman to walk about in naked . . . nobody looking on except the birds, and every one of them thinking that Paradise is back again, blackbirds and thrushes, willow wrens and warblers of all kinds, just as it was in the days when Marban spoke of the birds as the little musicians of the world to his brother, King Guaire, who came to see him' (p. 231).

As in medieval story the 'fearsome wood' is the antithesis to the friendly forest of Cummins and Marban, where communion exists between humans and nature, so in the same panel of the triptych in which he presents the inviting sanctuary of the friendly forest Moore also evokes the image of the threatening and alien dark wood. From Marban's tale in *A Story-Teller's Holiday* we learn that a madman of the dark woods may have stolen a fawn from the fleeing pair (p. 143). And earlier Marban is reminded that should he succumb to the temptation of a naked abbess that he could be driven into the wilderness, 'a bad place at night', full of wolves and bears (p. 110).

From out of the fearsome forest comes Alec Trusselby's blackthorn stick called 'the Murrigan', which whirled over his head like a bird, dipping occasionally to prod and poke humans. Although the Westport locals don't know the meaning of 'Murrigan', it is in truth a loathsome creature taken by Moore from Meyer's translation of *Reicne Fothaid Chanainne*, 'The Tryst after Death.'[17] In this early Irish poem the crow-raven goddess called the Morrigan is described washing the entrails of warriors at a stream's edge while she utters her terrible laugh. In the words of the poem, 'it is a stout heart that will not quail at her'.[18] The numerous *ceilleachs* of medieval Irish and Scottish-Gaelic folk tradition (including the Old Woman of Beare) owe much to the Morrigan. One Scottish-Gaelic ballad tells of the *Muilidheartach* who crossed the sea to oppose the Fenians, and her association with the fearsome wood is established in these lines:

> In her head was one deep pool-like eye
> swifter than a star in a winter sky;
> upon her head gnarled brushwood
> like the clawed old wood of aspen root.[19]

Tadgh and Ulick never encounter the like of the Morrigan, but they do traverse an 'evil wood', a forest that is full of 'fallen trees' and 'quaking trees, unable to stand, like men coming out of a tavern after midnight'. The knight and his harper move fearfully through a 'crapulous wood' that is fraught with pools and 'stinking rooks and nettles'; it is a place that holds a threat of violence because wolves may live there; and it is a lonesome place without a bird in it. 'I'm always afraid of a birdless wood' says Tadgh to Sir Ulick (pp. 90–91).

Again, in *Héloïse and Abélard*, Moore invokes the medieval image of the fearsome forest when Abelard, Heloise, and Madelon come to a place described as '. . . at the world's end' where '. . . they saw a blasted oak and a few pines at the end of a desolate track filled with great rocks'; '. . . a desolate place . . . visited only by the winds' (I, p. 211). This scene prepares them for their meeting with the wolf-hunter who pursued his grim calling in the fearsome forest. As they ride on 'through endless aisles' they are suddenly confronted with a club-flourishing peasant, 'a savage fellow' similar to the peasant encountered in the French medieval romance *Aucassin and Nicolette*.

COURTLY LOVE AND SPIRITUAL LOVE

The subject of the last panel in Moore's triptych is the medieval antithesis between courtly love – the permissive adultery celebrated in troubadour lyrics – and the fiercely spiritual and ascetic love promoted by monastic Christianity. Moore's exploration of the tensions provoked by these opposites is revealed in the character of John Norton, who began life in Moore's early novella, *A Mere Accident* (1887), reappeared in a short story bearing his name in *Celibates* (1895), and was reborn in *In Single Strictness* (1922) as Hugh Monfret. A dreamy aesthete who seeks refuge in the Middle Ages, Norton is introduced surrounded by stained glass, religious prints, carved oak cabinets, and 'high-backed chairs gleaming with Utrecht velvet' (*Celibates*, p. 326). Ironically, Norton muses over his qualifications for knighthood: 'I should have fought for the

Grail, like Parsifal', not for a lady love in a tournament. And after all, were not the Crusades as 'real in life as tennis parties are today . . . and infinitely more beautiful' (p. 335)? Nothing would have been more pleasant for Norton than to 'reconstruct the ascetic life of the Middle Ages . . . that would make meaning in his life' (p. 338). He embraces the monastic doctrine of contempt for the world, particularly its women, the *Femina dulce malum* of the cloisters. For Norton the curate's daughter Kitty Hare was not even 'sweet evil' but 'the vilest of evils'. Never could they have married, for then 'they would have had to part and would have been a "new Abelard – a new Heloise!" ' (p.451). In short, Moore's John Norton is an emotionally repressed young man, infatuated by the excessive morality, self-denial, and martyrdom preached by monastic Christianity and reflected at its harshest in the lives of the Irish saints and in the early Irish penitentials. But he is still a contemporary figure on whom the shadow of a medieval dilemma has fallen in modern times, and for that reason he provides an ironic contrast to the lustful Abélard before his mutilation and the womanizing Sir Ulick determined to snatch a willing Irish princess nun from her convent.

The tension and conflict generated by the unacceptability of each kind of love to advocates of its opposite in the Middle Ages motivates much of the action of *A Story-Teller's Holiday*. Liadin and Cuirithir fail the test placed on them by the hermit, Cummins, when Liadin casts a sleeping spell on the altar boy that Cummins has ordered to lie between them through the night. Cuirithir is sent to Rome to seek absolution; Liadin dies, falling from a rock into the lake as she watches Cuirithir's departure. Brother Marban passes excruciating tests of his vow of chastity in a monastery, where he sleeps each night with a different sister in order to help him up 'the difficult way to heaven' (p. 106). He fails his test with the beautiful young novice Luachet. Father Scothine, who took to the woods to escape human company and found his way to seaside crags where he lived off gulls' eggs, lay every night on the naked crags, doing penance. On his return his power of abstention is challenged by a woman of the parish who offers her two daughters, each to lie naked on either side of him.[20] In the same tale, Brenainn the monk fights temptation by immersing himself to his neck in a cistern of cold water – a favourite self-inflicted ordeal of the Irish ascetic.

Ironically, the emotional stresses endured by the partners in the cult of erotic love of twelfth-century France are as painful as those suffered by Irish monastic ascetics of earlier centuries, the same figures with whom they share the last panel of Moore's triptych. In true courtly love tradition Moore's trouvères in *Héloïse and Abélard* all pursue loves for which there is no hope of fulfillment because the canon dictates that true love can only be experienced outside of marriage. Denis the gleeman is hopelessly in love with the Countess d'Urgel; Jean Guiscard (modelled by Moore after the troubadour, Pierre Vidal) will never capture the Lady Louve; Godfrey Rudel, who left Provence on an ill-fated search for the Irish Princess Idena of Rathmoule, will die in Ireland, his love unrequited.[21] In perhaps Moore's own fantasy of courtly love,[22] Gauceln d'Arembert, having once enjoyed an idyll, must now be separated from Lady Malberge, whom he will only glimpse from afar as she presides over a Court of Love at Chatelleraud. Although love with physical fulfillment is granted to Héloïse and Abélard, it is followed by years of desolate separation. In Ireland, the poet-lovers Liadin and Cuirithir enjoy their passion in a 'place where the grass was thick under the larches . . . he not wearying and she nothing loth' (p. 77). It is clear that Liadin's words as translated by Meyer had their impact on Moore:

> A roaring flame
> has dissolved this heart of mine——
> Without him for certain it cannot live.[23]

But the two lovers hear the harsh voice of the priest in the land after their passionate embrace in the shadow of a druid's stone: 'Ireland will go back to the devil and the druids if we don't put a stop to that one . . .' (p. 79). Marban and his vibrant Luachet exchange brief rapture for a cruel and agonizing end when they are devoured by wolves before they can accomplish their escape.

Moore tried to justify, if not explain, the dilemma posed for men and women living under the strain of these medieval opposites. In a scene from *Ulick and Soracha* Ulick tells Tadgh: 'There must always be a barrier between the lover and the beloved . . .; the trouvère does no more than to love the lady in the castle as the monks and nuns in the cloister love the saints in heaven' (p. 108). At another point, Ulick observes 'We must suffer if we would enjoy, Tadgh; martyrs and trouvères are alike in this' (p. 109). When Tadgh predicts that his priest will tell him that 'no man should sing the praises of any wife but his own', Ulick urges him: 'Speak to him, Tadgh, of the need for a barrier' (p. 109).

Carefully inserted in the interstices of all three panels of Moore's triptych are vignettes, artifacts, allusions, and sketches from the medieval panorama. In *Héloïse and Abélard* it is the pilgrimage with its relic-selling pardoner; hunting hawks sweeping down on herons; a leper who was once a gleeman; ravenous wolves; Crusade lore; the realism-nominalism debate; the heady intellectual atmosphere of the Paris lecture halls; the cult of Virgil; the flaying alive of robbers; the sound of a lute; and the church bells of Paris. From *Ulick and Soracha* and *A Story-Teller's Holiday* come allusions to figures from the earliest Irish story cycles (Deirdre, Finn, Diarmuid and Grania, and Cuchullain); the devastation of true medieval warfare; lonely castles in Mayo and Galway; the making of an Irish harp; the merits of wine and mead. All these details enhance, never diminish, Moore's dominant themes. Contrary to the assertion that it is a 'keening' over the 'Celtic Twilight',[24] the theme of 'The Ruin of Ireland', as employed by Moore in the first panel of the triptych, is a sustained artistic effort to describe the destruction visited on Ireland from earliest times through the beginning of the twentieth century and to suggest that the calamities stem partly from lack of collective purpose and loss of effective leadership. In the second panel it is not 'wistful Celtic folk' whom we see, but individual men and women who are outcasts or exiles from a perpetually turbulent and unstable society. On one day these lovers, madmen, and displaced people may enjoy the sanctuary of the friendly forest; on another, they may be banished by a turn of Lady Fortune's wheel to the savage wood. Finally, in the third panel, the trouvères and their ladiés from *Héloïse and Abélard* are also creatures of the turmoil of the Middle Ages and captives of its antithesis between spiritual and erotic love. It is important to see them not as distracting elements in that novel but as a reflection of Moore's sympathy for individual men and women living in any society that engenders repression and frustration. Neither does Moore's sly and earthy treatment of the Irish monks and their temptresses in *A Story-Teller's Holiday* conceal his empathy for human beings.

Moore's triptych and its interrelated traditional medieval themes reach us through the simulated words of the seanachie and in imitation of the slow-paced, circuitous, digressive style of medieval narrative. In the end, oral and written tradition work magic for George Moore: they transform his triptych into a *speculum* – a mirror in which twentieth century Ireland might see itself.

NOTES

1   The editions used in the preparation of this essay are: George Moore, *A Story-Teller's Holiday* (London, 1918) [Privately printed for subscribers only by Cumann Sean-eolais na h-Éireann]; *Héloïse and Abélard*, 2 vols. (London,

1921) [Privately printed for subscribers only by Cumann Sean-eolais na h-Eireann]; *Ulick and Soracha* (New York: Boni and Liveright, 1926). *Ulick and Soracha*, with some revisions, was included by Moore in the Uniform Edition of *A Story-Teller's Holiday*, 2 vols. (London: Heinemann, 1928). Also used were 'Perronik the Fool', in *Daphnis and Chloë and Perronik the Fool*, Carra Edition (New York: Boni and Liveright, 1924); 'John Norton,' in *Celibates* (London: Walter Scott, 1895), pp. 315–452; and 'Hugh Monfret' in *In Single Strictness* (New York: Boni and Liveright, 1922).

2 See Francis L. Nye, 'George Moore's Use of Sources in *Héloïse and Abélard*', *English Literature in Transition* 18, 3 (1975), 161–180.

3 Kuno Meyer (1858–1919), noted Germanist and Celtic scholar, Professor in the University of Liverpool, 1884–1911, who succeeded Heinrich Zimmer in the chair of Celtic at Berlin. Meyer was one of the founders and first Director of the School of Irish Learning in Dublin and editor of its journal, *Ériu*. Moore presented a whimsical and sympathetic picture of him in *Hail and Farewell*, II (New York: Boni and Liveright, 1925), p. 26. Moore claimed to have first met Meyer on the occasion of the performance of *The Tinker and the Fairy* in his Dublin garden in 1903.

4 Malcolm Brown, *George Moore: A Reconsideration* (Seattle, University of Washington Press, 1955) p. xi, p. 169.

5 Janet F. Egleson [Dunleavy], 'The Heritage of Moore Hall',' *An Féinisc* (1968), 54.

6 Edmund Curtis (1881–1943), brilliant Oxford-trained historian who had been appointed Professor of Modern History at Trinity College Dublin in 1914. He acquired a working knowledge of Irish, was a Gaelic nationalist in sympathy who also was proud of his Protestant 'planter' ancestry. On Moore's friendship with Curtis, see Joseph Hone, *The Life of George Moore* (New York: Macmillan, 1936), pp. 386–88. Curtis's *History of Medieval Ireland* (Dublin, 1923), particularly Chapter IX, 'The Second Irish Resurgence', provided Moore with the historical background of fourteenth-century Ireland that he needed for the writing of *Ulick and Soracha*.

7 *Selections from Ancient Irish Poetry*, trans. Kuno Meyer (London, 1928), pp. 90–93.

8 In a note to Mrs. Virginia Crawford, who had helped him with the details of costume and architecture in the writing of *Héloïse and Abélard*, Moore says that he invented the episode of the finding of Arthur in the ruined hall. See Hone, *Life*, p. 358. Moore admired William Morris's *The Defence of Guinevere*; 'one of the most beautiful things in English poetry . . . The Tomb of Arthur* I like better', he wrote to Nancy Cunard.

9 For trees, groves, and woods as sacred places among the Celts see Anne Ross, *Pagan Celtic Britain* (London, 1967), pp. 33–38. Jean Markale comments on the association of women with forests, orchards, and virgin woods as places of seclusion and refuge, possibly connecting them to the Garden of Paradise. See *Women of the Celts* (London, 1975), pp. 75–78.

10 Moore's chief source for the Suibhne Geilt material was J.G. O'Keeffe's *Buile Suibhne (The Frenzy of Suibhne)* Irish Texts Society, XII (London, 1913). In a letter to Richard Irvine Best in 1917, Moore wrote: 'The story of the Madman fills me with despair, so wonderful it is, so much beyond the reach of the modern story-teller . . . the abridged version does not satisfy me. I want the full text . . . and am willing to pay for it'. Hone, *Life*, p. 335. Best (1872–1959) was a Celtic scholar who had studied Old Irish in Paris where he had met Synge and Kuno Meyer. He was Assistant Director of the National Library of Ireland from 1904 and Director from 1924. He later served as Chairman of the Irish Manuscripts

Commission and President of the Royal Irish Academy. See Hone, *Life*, p. 335, for Best's assistance to Moore in the writing of *A Story-Teller's Holiday*. For Best and Moore's longtime friendship, see Hone, *passim*.

11   See *Early Irish Lyrics*, ed. and trans. Gerard Murphy (Oxford, 1956), p. 129.
12   Ibid.
13   Ibid., p. 137.
14   Austin Clarke, 'A Visit with George Moore', in *The Man of Wax* ed. Douglas A. Hughes (New York, 1971), pp. 52–53.
15   Meyer, *Selections*, pp. 47–50.
16   Compare Moore's lines with Meyer's translation in *Selections*, p. 50.
17   Meyer, *Selections*, p. 111.
18   Ibid.,
19   Ross, *Pagan Celtic Britain*, p. 233.
20   See Vivian Mercier, *The Irish Comic Tradition* (Oxford, 1969), p. 42, who calls the temptations of Father Scothine the 'only one of Moore's humorous stories . . . which seems to have a firm basis in Irish tradition'. The medieval Irish source for the temptation scene is the Old Irish *Martyrology of Oengus the Culdee* ed. and trans. Whitley Stokes (London, 1905), p. 41: 'Now two maidens with pointed breasts used to lie with him every night that the battle with the Devil might be the greater for him'. On the struggles of early Irish clerics with temptation see also Gareth W. Dunleavy, *Colum's Other Island: The Irish at Lindisfarne* (Madison, 1960), pp. 87–91.
21   Nye, 'George Moore's Use of Sources in *Héloïse and Abélard*,' pp. 164–65, points out that in the source where Moore may have found the tale, Idena is a princess of Tripoli, not Ireland. Moore's most striking innovation according to Nye is that he makes Abélard a gleeman. Nye notes also that troubadours and trouvères flourished in the second rather than the first half of the twelfth century.
22   In a letter of 14 Oct 1932 to Lady Cunard (Maude Burke) asking her to read Chaps. XX and XXI of *Héloïse and Abélard*, Moore wrote: 'In the woods around Franchard you will meet the hermit who is I masquerading under the name Gaucelm d'Arembert, and yourself under the name of the Lady Malberge'. *George Moore: Letters to Lady Cunard*, 1895–1933, ed. Rupert Hart-Davis (London, 1957), p. 194.
23   Meyer, *Selections*, p. 66.
24   Brown, *George Moore: A Reconsideration*, pp. 169–70.

THE MOORE-JOYCE NEXUS: AN IRISH LITERARY COMEDY

PATRICK A. McCARTHY

There is by now a long list of studies of George Moore's complex relationship to James Joyce. In recent years critics have uncovered extensive parallels between *The Untilled Field* and *Dubliners*, examined the possible influence of *Confessions of a Young Man* on *A Portrait of the Artist as a Young Man*, and pointed to a host of more or less credible allusions to Moore's writing hidden in the pages of *Ulysses*. In the search for parallels and allusions one critic seeks to top another: when Robert M. Adams discovers a parody of Father Oliver Gogarty's buttocks in the black mass sequence of *Ulysses*, Anthony Farrow adds, somewhat less persuasively, that the buttocks may also be found on St. Kevin in *Finnegans Wake*.[1] Inevitably repeated in the course of these analyses, Joyce's and Moore's comments on one another have become familiar material: Joyce's sneer at Moore as 'a genuine gent/That lives on his property's ten per cent'[2] and Moore's riposte that Joyce was 'nobody – from the Dublin docks: no family, no breeding'[3] are cited and recited as evidence of the antagonism between the two writers. Unfortunately there has been little progress made toward reconciling the two aspects of this Irish literary comedy, no real attempt to trace the connexion between Joyce's literary response to his Irish precursor and their uneasy, at times hostile, personal relationship. In this study of the Moore-Joyce nexus I shall contend that although Joyce was indeed influenced by Moore (although not particularly by *Confessions of a Young Man*, despite Moore's claim), professional jealousy, insecurity, and the memory of being ignored by Moore while he was in Dublin prevented Joyce from acknowledging a major literary debt.

Apart from the differences in social class, which were by no means quite so great as both Moore and Joyce seemed to think, the two writers had much in common. Both were Irish Catholics who rejected their religion and went into self-imposed exile (although by the time Joyce entered the Dublin literary scene Moore had returned to Ireland); both were influenced in their youth by the

Romantics and later by literary realism and *fin de siècle*
Aestheticism; both were self-styled despisers of the rabble; both
came increasingly to break with the English tradition in the novel
and to feel the influence of poetry, painting, and music on their
works. The models for the kind of fiction they wrote came most
often from outside England and Ireland: when Stanislaus Joyce
listed the writers his brother was 'eagerly' reading at the turn of the
century, George Moore's name appeared prominently in the
company of Tolstoy, Turgenev, D'Annunzio, Verlaine, Maeter-
linck, and Sudermann, the only other English-speaking writers in
the catalogue being poets (Yeats, Mangan, Blake, Shakespeare).[4]
For that matter, Graham Hough's description of Moore's aesthetic
goals applies equally well to Joyce:

Three steady preoccupations can be discerned among his shifting
allegiances: one is with telling the truth about experience instead of merely
devising an agreeable story; the second is with imaginative freedom . . .; the
third is with formal justness and beauty in expression and organization,
instead of the labored or slapdash approximations to which the English
novel in all but its highest moments had been prone.[5]

In their comments on one another, their kinship occasionally
surfaced. Moore found Joyce's 1901 broadside, 'The Day of the
Rabblement', 'preposterously clever', according to Russell,[6] and
one might suspect that Moore's approval of the piece – delivered by
Stanislaus Joyce to Moore's servant – had less to do with Joyce's
comments on Moore himself than with the polemical excess of
Joyce's opening: 'No man, says the Nolan, can be a lover of the true
or the good unless he abhors the multitude; and the artist, though he
may employ the crowd, is very careful to isolate himself'.[7] Joyce's
protest against 'making terms with the rabblement' had in fact been
made by Moore thirteen years earlier, in *Confessions of a Young
Man*, when he contended that 'Art is the direct antithesis to
democracy . . . The mass can only appreciate simple and *naïve*
emotions, puerile prettiness, above all conventionalities'.[8] For his
part, Joyce praised Moore in a 1907 essay written in Trieste, where
his appreciation for Irish writers was considerably greater than it
was when they were across town from him: six years after passing
Moore off as someone who 'is beginning to draw upon his literary
account' (that is, to repeat himself), Joyce found Moore 'an
intellectual oasis in the Sahara of the false spiritualistic, Messianic,
and detective writings whose name is legion in England'.[9] Moore
seemed to get better as Joyce grew older, so that by the time he was

working on *Ulysses* Joyce was able to describe *Esther Waters* as 'the best novel of modern English life'.[10]

Despite this intermittent civility, the two writers more often found reason to take potshots at one another's work. Although occasionally humourous, the barbs are generally petty, and few can be accepted without some qualification. Joyce concluded his treatment of Moore in 'The Day of the Rabblement' with the flat assertion that Moore's 'new impulse has no kind of relation to the future of art', and Moore probably remembered the comment thirty years later when he wrote to Louis Gillet that *Ulysses* 'has nothing to do with art'.[11] Joyce criticized 'George Moore, the Parisian' for admiring Dostoevsky; Moore, now firmly in his anti-Zola stage, called the author of *A Portrait of the Artist* 'a sort of Zola gone to seed' and asked why Joyce would bother writing such a book, one 'entirely without style or distinction', when Moore had done 'the same thing, but much better, in *The Confessions of a Young Man*'.[12] Moore also found the *Dubliners* stories generally 'trivial and disagreeable', although 'The Dead', he believed, 'seemed to me perfection whilst I read it!'[13] Joyce's remarks about *The Untilled Field* were considerably more intemperate. He first expressed his dislike for the book in a letter to Stanislaus dated November 1904, although there is good reason to suppose that he had read it much earlier. By September 1905 he was still sufficiently incensed by the volume to call it 'that silly, wretched book of Moore's . . . which the Americans found so remarkable for its "craftsmanship". O, dear me! It is very dull and flat, indeed: and ill written'.[14] In the earlier letter he had specified some of the collection's artistic faults:

I have read Moore's 'Untilled Field' in Tauchnitz. Damned stupid. A woman alludes to her husband in the confession-box as 'Ned'. Ned thinks &c! A lady who has been living for three years on the line between Bray and Dublin is told by her husband that there is a meeting in Dublin at which he must be present. She looks up the table to see the hours of the trains. This on DW and WR where the trains go regularly: this after three years. Isn't it rather stupid of Moore. And the punctuation! Madonna![15]

Critics have referred to this letter without examining its allegations carefully. The most general of the charges, that Moore's punctuation is sloppy, could be made about many writers of the day: D. H. Lawrence often punctuated English sentences as if they were French, and Joyce himself omitted commas that others might consider essential. Joyce's other points seem even less convincing. To a very formal man like Joyce it might have been inconceivable that a woman could ever refer to her husband by his first name while in confession, but in 'The Wild Goose' the single instance of this usage seems realistic. It occurs when Ellen Carmady says to Father Brennan, 'Ned and I never talk politics; we used to, but that is a long time ago' (UF, 364).[16] In the context of the discussion, which is not precisely a normal confession because Ellen is asking for advice rather than genuinely confessing her sins, it appears natural for Ellen to call her husband 'Ned', especially since the priest has just called him 'Mr Carmady'. Joyce's objection to the scene in which Ellen picks up the train schedule is equally dubious, for only a person who often rode trains or knew others who often rode them would know their schedule: a stay-at-home like Ellen might be forgiven for having to recheck the precise times.

The fact is that Joyce's attack on *The Untilled Field* had less to do with the quality of Moore's book than with Joyce's own situation and artistic ambition. Herbert Howarth surely overstates his case when he claims that '*Dubliners* is another *Untilled Field*', but he is on target in noting resemblances between the two collections: 'they both attack the dirt of Ireland, and the ignorance they make it represent; and they both catch a Russian quality, which Moore had deliberately borrowed from Turgenev, and which Joyce now borrowed from Moore'. Howarth is accurate, too, in stating that 'Joyce was jealous at the likeness . . . He did not want to have an Irish Catholic precursor'.[17] Although *The Untilled Field* met with considerably less resentment than *Dubliners*, it is also worth noting that in attacking 'the dirt of Ireland' Moore and Joyce found themselves equally open to the charge that the dirt was in their books, and ultimately in their minds. The charge was made most memorably by Sir John Mahaffy, who declared, 'Thank God, [Moore and Joyce] have both cleared out of Dublin, but not before they had squirted stink like a pair of skunks on all the decent people . . . It's an ill bird that fouls its own nest'.[18] In publishing his own collection of short stories a decade later than Moore's, Joyce was determined to draw even more attention to what he saw as defects in the Irish character, even if he risked widespread condemnation on the grounds that he was a nest-fouler.

Joyce told his publisher that his book was 'a chapter of the moral history' of Ireland, written 'in a style of scrupulous meanness' and with absolute fidelity to what he saw and heard in Dublin.[19] Although Janet Dunleavy states quite accurately that Moore's Dublin stories are stylistically inferior to the tales of the Irish countryside,[20] in the best stories Moore's style is also a carefully honed instrument. Like Joyce, Moore was sometimes able to write stories in a language that is 'lean and muscular, the product . . . of slow and scrupulous revision; erasing, as it were, all that does not tell'.[21] Such a style emerges, for instance, in the description of the town at the end of 'Julia Cahill's Curse':

> It stood in the middle of a flat country, and as we approached it the great wall of the cathedral rose above dirty and broken cottages, and great masses of masonry extended from the cathedral into the town; and these were the nunnery, its schools and laundry; altogether they seemed like one great cloud. (UF, 220)

Throughout most of *Dubliners* the style is equally 'lean and muscular', as in this description of Little Chandler's inability to escape his child's crying so that he could read a poem by Byron:

> It was useless. He couldn't read. He couldn't do anything. The wailing of the child pierced the drum of his ear. It was useless, useless! He was a prisoner for life. His arms trembled with anger and suddenly bending to the child's face he shouted:
> –Stop!
> The child stopped for an instant, had a spasm of fright and began to scream. He jumped up from his chair and walked hastily up and down the room with the child in his arms. It began to sob piteously, losing its breath for four or five seconds, and then bursting out anew ... (D, 84)[22]

Joyce maintains this tone more consistently than Moore, and invests his descriptions more often with ironic overtones. A slightly odd phrasing like the opening of 'Eveline' – 'She sat at the window watching the evening invade the avenue' – is almost always meaningful in *Dubliners*: here, for example, Joyce calls attention to the idea of invasion in a story that will end in Eveline's failed attempt to emigrate, and thereby subtly contrasts the two great demographic movements that have dominated Irish history. Eveline's avenue is 'invaded' (and we soon learn that 'a man from Belfast' has bought the field on which the children once played, so that Joyce seems to be thinking of the English rather than the Viking invasion of Ireland), but Eveline will have no avenue of escape from her imprisonment. Again and again, Joyce's phrasing works on at least two levels, as when the opening sentence of 'The Dead' – 'Lily, the caretaker's daughter, was literally run off her feet' – not only introduces the theme of death in comic fashion but serves as an ironic comment on the use of language in a society in which 'literally' is used to mean its opposite, 'figuratively'. Such touches are rare in *The Untilled Field*, but they are not entirely absent. A small example comes at the end of 'A Letter to Rome', when Father MacTurnan leaves the Bishop's house blissfully unaware that the

Bishop has not discussed the reception at the Vatican of his letter about the marriage of priests. He awakens James Murdoch to tell him that he has collected the five pounds Murdoch needs to marry, and the simple final statement – 'The poor man came stumbling across the bog, and the priest told him the news' – says worlds about the relationship between the poor man and the even poorer priest who believes he can awaken people to the news of their salvation but who is really trapped in the same bog as they are.

Various critics have pointed to specific parallels between stories in the two collections: between Moore's 'In the Clay' and Joyce's 'Clay',[23] between 'The Wild Goose' and 'The Dead',[24] and between several other stories.[25] Occasionally suggestive of direct influence, these parallels more often are simply evidence that Joyce and Moore saw the same problems in Ireland: parochialism, prudery, the influence of a conservative priesthood, the ignorance of the average Irishman. Joyce, however, is considerably more pessimistic than Moore: whereas Moore wrote several stories depicting the pathos of exile, Joyce goes one step further and describes people who are trapped in Dublin despite their desire to escape to more exotic locales.

Likewise *Dubliners* has a tighter organization than *The Untilled Field*, although again Joyce was simply more successful at achieving an effect that Moore had previously sought. While she correctly notes that Moore overestimated the unity of his book, Deborah Averill also observes that Joyce and Moore both followed the example of Turgenev's *Hunting Sketches* in attempting to unify their works through such devices as 'a shared location, overlapping characters, and repetition of a central theme'.[26] Moore certainly conceived of the book as 'not a mere collection of short stories' but 'a book about Ireland . . . in the form of short stories', and he boasted to his publisher that 'The book is a perfect unity'.[27] In the first English edition of *The Untilled Field*, Moore reinforced the effect of unified structure by introducing themes and characters in his first story, 'In the Clay', and returning to them in 'The Way Back', the final story of the volume. Joyce made even more elaborate use of circular structure. For example, the conclusion of 'The Dead' ironically echoes the opening of the first story in *Dubliners*, 'The Sisters': both passages involve a character standing before a 'lighted square of window' at night, and when the boy finds the old priest's window lighted 'faintly and evenly' the book sends out a verbal signal that will be echoed back in the final description of the snow 'falling faintly through the universe and faintly falling' in a uniform pattern across Ireland. Unlike Moore, Joyce develops this image of circularity into a recurrent emblem of the characters' entrapment; in *The Untilled Field*, on the other hand, the framing device suggests the possibility of escape, since Rodney's reappearance in 'The Way Back' is only a temporary return to Ireland on the way between London and Italy.

Moore's own favourite story in *Dubliners* was 'The Dead', and much of the critical attention lavished on the Joyce-Moore relationship has focused on Moore's possible influence on this story. Richard Ellmann has suggested that the final scene of Joyce's story, in which the shadow of Gretta's long-dead lover comes between her and her husband, is based on the conclusion of *Vain Fortune*, a novel that Joyce had praised in 'The Day of the Rabblement'.[28] Joyce's praise for that novel might seem odd, particularly in view of Moore's own evaluation of it as 'a weak wretched thing'[29] (although *Vain Fortune* at least has a character, Hubert Price, who knows a train schedule without having to look it up[30]); but Joyce found in the book situations and characters that stimulated his imagination. Ellmann correctly observes that 'The dead lover who comes between the lovers, the sense of the husband's failure, the acceptance of mediocrity, the resolve to be at all events sympathetic, all come from *Vain Fortune*'. A more specific parallel might be found in Emily's 'I am dying of love for you' (VF, 234), which is echoed in Gretta Conroy's statement about Michael Furey, 'I think he died for me' (D, 220). It is also striking to contrast the following passage,

. . . [Hubert] looked at his wife. She seemed to him very beautiful as she slept, her face turned a little on one side, and he asked himself if he loved her. Then, going to the window, he drew the curtains softly, so as not to awaken her; and as he stood watching a thin, discoloured day now breaking over the roofs, it seemed to him that Emily's suicide was the better part . . . Should he ever be happy any more? Surely Emily's suicide was the better part. (VF, 283)

with the conclusion of Joyce's story. There, as Gretta sleeps, Gabriel watches her 'as though he and she had never lived together as man and wife' (just as Hubert and Julia have not consummated their marriage). Contrasting Michael Furey's half-suicidal death with the half-life of his Aunt Julia, whose name might derive from *Vain Fortune*, and thinking also of his own passionless existence, Gabriel thinks, 'Better pass boldly into that other world, in the full glory of some passion, than fade and wither dismally with age'. Finally he realizes that unlike Michael, he has never really loved Gretta: 'He had never felt like that towards any woman but he knew that such a feeling must be love' (D, 222–23).

As Anita Gandolfo has noted, however, *Vain Fortune* was not Moore's only contribution to the shaping of 'The Dead', for there are also significant parallels between Joyce's story and the first story in *Celibates*, 'Mildred Lawson', a story that Joyce liked well enough to want to translate into Italian.[31] Likewise, Patricia McFate has called attention to correspondences between 'The Wild Goose' and 'The Dead', although she also detects a crucial difference between the male protagonists of the stories: 'Ned Carmady, the *wild* goose, is strong enough to leave Ireland, but his strength comes from his egocentrism. . . Gabriel Conroy, the *tame* goose, is strong enough to stay in Ireland, for his strength is in his humanity, his final vision of the indissoluble linkages of all times and all men.'[32] Given the careful attention paid to Moore's influence on various aspects of 'The Dead' (particularly its conclusion), it is a little surprising that no one has pointed to the line, 'The time had come for him to set out on his journey westward', as a possible reference to yet another work by Moore. In that work, *The Lake*, Father Oliver Gogarty writes to Rose Leicester (Nora Glynn in the revised edition) of his plan to stage his suicide and go to America and thinks that it is 'extraordinary . . . that he should be writing to Rose Leicester, who was going in search of the Christian river, while he was planning a journey westward'.[33]

Father Oliver's awakening to his subconscious desires broadly parallels Gabriel Conroy's sudden realization of the shallowness of his life, but *The Lake* is almost certainly more important for its influence on Joyce's later fiction. Ironically, when he discussed *The Lake* in his letters to his brother, Joyce found nothing in the book to praise. In August 1906 Joyce ridiculed the novel's plot, Rose Leicester's letters, the figure of Ralph Ellis (Walter Poole in the revised edition), Father Oliver's plunge into the lake, and the preface in French to Edouard Dujardin. A week later he sent Stanislaus a copy of the book, asking his opinion and trying to shape that opinion in the same letter by ridiculing a phrase from Moore's preface.[34] Two weeks later he was again on the attack:

Yerra, what's good in the end of *The Lake*? I see nothing. And what is to be said about the 'lithery' man, Ellis, and all the talk about pictures and music. Now, tell the God's truth, isn't it *bloody* tiresome? To me it is. As for 'Rev Oliver Gogarty' I think that may either have been laughingly suggested by O. St Jesus for his greater glory or hawkeyedly intended by Moore to put O. St Jesus in an *embarras*. . . Re Joycetown: there is I am sure some place of that name in the neighbourhood he writes of.[35]

A concluding scene in which a character named Oliver Gogarty swims to freedom on the Joycetown side of a lake should have made the novel irresistible to Joyce, yet he stubbornly refused to see the many virtues in this great work. The reason for Joyce's antipathy to *The Lake* is very close to the motive for Moore's later dislike of *Ulysses* (years before he had read it). Ezra Pound described Moore's reason bluntly in his essay, 'James Joyce et Pécuchet': 'Pour George Moore et Shaw, il est de la nature humaine de ne pas vouloir se voir éclipsé par un écrivain de plus grande importance qu'eux-mêmes.'[36] Similarly, it seems likely that in 1906 Joyce was seriously biased against a book in which Moore had solved some of the artistic problems that Joyce was failing to solve in his autobiographical novel, *Stephen Hero*. Indeed, by the time he read *The Lake* Joyce was bogged down in the writing of his rather formless novel. This was for Joyce a very frustrating time: he had written all of *Dubliners* except 'The Dead', which was not part of the original plan for the collection, but the book had been rejected by Grant Richards seven months after being tentatively accepted. Joyce wrote to Stanislaus from Rome, where he was working as a bank clerk after his position at the Berlitz school in Trieste fell through, and the unsettled nature of his personal life made it difficult to see his way to the new approach he needed to take in his novel if it were to record the 'fluid succession of presents' he alluded to in his early essay, 'A Portrait of the Artist'.

When he began work on the revised novel, *A Portrait of the Artist as a Young Man*, in late 1907, Joyce almost certainly had in mind some of the lessons he had learned from *The Lake*. The most important influence of Moore's novel, in all likelihood, was on Joyce's turn to overtly impressionistic techniques in the *Portrait*.[37] The style of *Stephen Hero* is by comparison direct and old fashioned, quite at odds with Joyce's goal of truly revealing the contours of Stephen's consciousness. The directness is evident in a typical passage:

The very morning after this Father Butt returned Stephen's monologue in kind. It was a raw nipping morning and when Stephen, who had arrived too late for the Latin lecture, strolled into the Physics Theatre he discovered Father Butt kneeling on the hearthstone engaged in lighting a small fire in the huge grate. He was making neat wisps of paper and carefully disposing them among the coals and sticks. All the while he kept up a little patter explaining his operations and at a crisis he produced from the most remote pockets of his chalkey soutane three dirty candle-butts. These he thrust in different openings and then looked up at Stephen with an air of triumph. He set a match to a few projecting pieces of paper and in a few minutes the coals had caught.[38]

In a parallel passage in *A Portrait of the Artist* Joyce turns quickly to the impression the scene makes on Stephen's mind:

> [The dean of studies] produced four candlebutts from the sidepockets of his soutane and placed them deftly among the coals and twisted papers. Stephen watched him in silence. Kneeling thus on the flagstone to kindle the fire and busied with the disposition of his wisps of paper and candlebutts he seemed more than ever a humble server making ready the place of sacrifice in an empty temple, a levite of the Lord. Like a levite's robe of plain linen the faded worn soutane draped the kneeling figure of one whom the canonicals or the bellbordered ephod would irk and trouble. His very body had waxed old in lowly service of the Lord . . . Nay, his very soul had waxed old in that service without growing towards light and beauty or spreading abroad a sweet odour of her sanctity. . . (P, 185)[39]

That this impressionistic style may be traced to *The Lake* seems even more likely when it is realized that one of Joyce's most significantly impressionistic stories is 'The Dead', which was composed between Joyce's reading of *The Lake* and his first revisions of *A Portrait of the Artist*, and which contained a small reference to *The Lake* in the phrase 'journey westward'. In that story Joyce allowed Gabriel's vision of himself and his environment to colour the narration of the events, yet allowed the readers to view Gabriel both ironically and sympathetically. Moore had achieved the same effect in *The Lake*, and Joyce was to repeat it in the *Portrait*. Moore's repeated references to the lake become highly significant when the reader understands that this is not mere description but the selection of significant detail which at once illuminates the character's mind and allows the reader to view Father Oliver from a slightly ironic perspective: we know, long before Father Oliver does, that his repressed sexuality is the cause of his complex attitude toward Nora Glynn, and that in constantly edging around the lake he is revealing his fear of the life that the lake represents. At the beginning the lake is seen vaguely, as if in response to the inability of the priest to look directly at himself: 'The lake lay like a mirror that somebody had breathed upon, the brown islands showing through the mist faintly, with gray shadows falling in the water, blurred at the edges' (L, 1). At the end, however, the meaning of the lake becomes explicit to character and reader alike: 'On the deck of the steamer he heard the lake's warble above the violence of the waves. "There is a lake in every man's heart," he said, "and he listens to its monotonous whisper year by year, more and more attentive till at last he ungirds" ' (L, 179).

Joyce pronounced himself immune to the beauties of *The Lake's* conclusion, but his work was profoundly influenced by Moore's subtle use of repeated images and other impressionistic effects. Moore, in turn, was heavily influenced by Edouard Dujardin, to whom he dedicated *The Lake*, and, of course, by the example of Wagnerian music, a particular passion of Dujardin as well. Joyce's use of motifs in the *Portrait* and *Ulysses* has often been described as Wagnerian, and he claimed that his use of the *monologue intérieur* in *Ulysses* was inspired by Dujardin, but Moore was almost certainly one of the media through which Wagner and Dujardin exerted their influence on Joyce. Richard Ellmann tells us that Joyce bought Dujardin's *Les lauriers sont coupés* in France in 1903,[40] but the book made no immediate impact on Joyce's writing; and later, when he acknowledged his debt to Dujardin, he was merely admitting that he borrowed a formal narrative device – presentation of a character's thoughts directly, without an intervening narrator – from an author who had used the device less skilfully. Despite Linda Bennett's assertion that 'Moore uses the interior monologue in *The Lake*',[41] Moore never used the device in his works, preferring something closer to *style indirect libre*, in which an outside narrator is retained while the protagonist's consciousness is allowed to dominate the diction and selection of details in the narrative. (This, of course, is the point of view used throughout almost all of Joyce's *Portrait*.) What Moore learned from Dujardin, actually, is the great possibility of using impressionistic description; but as Richard Cave has noted, Moore improved upon *Les lauriers sont coupés* by making the reader 'aware, as the spectator is in viewing certain styles of painting, that a selection of sense-data has been made for a private subjective purpose. The nature of that purpose, that inner controlling force which determines the essence of a character at a given point in time, will reveal itself only gradually and by implication through the total pattern of the novel'.[42] Whatever stock we may place in Joyce's later claims for the influence of *Les lauriers sont coupés* on *Ulysses*, Dujardin's influence on *A Portrait of the Artist* was entirely indirect, for it is Moore rather than Dujardin whose narrative mode is closest to that of Joyce's early novel.

That debt may be signalled by other parallels between the two novels. In the broad sense, of course, each tells the story of a character who rejects the easy spiritual comfort and ascetic lifestyle of the priesthood for the more dangerous and fulfilling life of the world; both novels end on a triumphant note of spiritual liberation, although Joyce's conclusion is considerably tinged with irony; Stephen Dedalus is preparing to go into exile at the end of one book, while the other goes one step further by placing Father Oliver on the steamer to America; both novels use complex patterns of bird imagery to develop their themes. Ellmann is probably also correct when he suggests that in writing the famous scene at the end of the fourth chapter of the *Portrait*, in which Stephen watches a bird-like girl wading on the strand, Joyce recalled Father Oliver's liberating plunge into the lake: 'Stephen, like Father Gogarty, undergoes a rite of secular baptism, and Joyce's water and bird imagery, while he has made it altogether his own, seems to owe something to Moore's symbolism of lake, stagnant pool, and fluttering curlew'.[43]

Less convincing is the suggestion of another critic that Stephen and Father Oliver both 'suffer a single painful and humiliating experience of corporal punishment at school'.[44] Stephen actually receives two pandies from his teachers (P, 156), although we see only one of them, by Father Dolan; but since young Oliver is beaten by sadistic schoolmates who dare him to prove his desire to mortify his flesh (L, 12–13), the influence, if there was any, might more reasonably be seen either in Stephen's flaying by Heron, Boland, and Nash (P, 81–82) or in his later attempt to bring his senses 'under a rigorous discipline' (P, 150). More highly significant, perhaps, is Moore's travesty of Oliver's masochism, as he willingly bares his back to Tom Bryan, only to find that he has gotten more than he bargained for when Tom exchanges Oliver's small whip for 'a great leather belt'. An odd version of this sequence, one that openly develops the sexual implications underlying Moore's scene, may be found in the 'Circe' episode of *Ulysses*: threatened by Mrs. Mervyn Talboys, who promises, 'I'll scourge the pigeonlivered cur as long as I can stand over him. I'll flay him alive', Leopold Bloom first responds with excitement ('I love the danger') but soon gets cold feet, explaining, 'All these people. I meant only the spanking idea. A warm tingling glow without effusion. Refined birching to stimulate the circulation' (U, 467–68).[45]

There are, as it happens, somewhat more obvious allusions in *Ulysses* to *The Lake*, all of them dependent on our recognizing that Buck Mulligan, Stephen's roommate and rival, is based on Joyce's one-time friend, Oliver Gogarty. Moore's real reason for appropriating Gogarty's name for the protagonist of *The Lake* has not been satisfactorily explained, but whether or not Joyce was correct in suspecting that Moore intended to embarrass Gogarty, it is clear that Gogarty resented the use of his name.[46] Still, Moore borrowed only Gogarty's name, not his character, and tried to smooth matters over by telling Mrs. Gogarty, 'Madame supply me with two such joyous dactyls and I will gladly change the name' – a remark one critic credits with having inspired Mulligan's remark about his name: 'My name is absurd too: Malachi Mulligan, two dactyls' (U, 4).[47] If Joyce heard of Moore's comment, he might well have intended to call attention to Moore's lack of invention by coining another name in double dactyls. And in borrowing Gogarty's character but not his name, Joyce set up the possibility of numerous subtle contrasts between his Buck Mulligan and Moore's Father Oliver. The two characters seem almost mirror inversions of each other: Father Oliver's sensitivity is replaced, in *Ulysses*, by Mulligan's coarseness and blasphemy; the priest's attempt to save Father Moran from alcohol contrasts sharply with Buck Mulligan's determination to get Stephen Dedalus drunk; and even Mulligan's desire to Hellenise Ireland, to bring a foreign culture to his country, reverses the pattern of Father Oliver's great wish to leave Ireland.

The recognition of the Mulligan-Gogarty-Father Oliver link adds another level of enjoyment to the reading of Joyce's first chapter, 'Telemachus'. The chapter begins with Mulligan, Stephen, and the Englishman, Haines, all at the Martello Tower at Sandycove and concludes with Stephen walking to his job at Mr. Deasy's school. That Joyce had *The Lake* in mind when he wrote this chapter is made all the more likely in view of the fact that near the end of the episode Mulligan takes off his clothes and leaps into the bay, thereby recalling Father Oliver's jump into the lake; later, Joyce reinforces the association by having Stephen think of Mulligan's expertise in swimming. (Stephen, by contrast, neither swims nor bathes: his aversion to water is ultimately the product of a fear of life much as Father Oliver's continual skirting of the lake throughout most of the novel results from his own fears.) Like Father Oliver, Mulligan also begins the chapter as a priest, albeit a phony one:

Stately, plump Buck Mulligan came from the stairhead, bearing a bowl of lather on which a mirror and a razor lay crossed. A yellow dressinggown, ungirdled, was sustained gently behind him by the mild morning air. He held the bowl aloft and intoned:

——*Introibo ad altare Dei*.

Halted, he peered down the dark winding stairs and called up coarsely:

——Come up, Kinch. Come up, you fearful jesuit.

Solemnly he came forward and mounted the round gunrest. He faced about and blessed gravely thrice the tower, the surrounding country and the awaking mountains. Then, catching sight of Stephen Dedalus, he bent towards him and made rapid crosses in the air, gurgling in his throat and shaking his head . . . (U, 2–3)

Even here Joyce might be thinking not only of Father Oliver's role

as parish priest but of his eventual escape, for Mulligan's 'ungirdled'
dressinggown recalls the priest's last thoughts in *The Lake*: ' "There
is a lake in every man's heart," he said, "and he listens to its
monotonous whisper year by year, more and more attentive till at
last he ungirds" '.

It would be interesting to learn whether or not Joyce ever knew
that Moore had originally planned *The Lake* as a story for *The
Untilled Field*, since the idea that Joyce developed into *Ulysses* was,
in the beginning, supposed to be for a *Dubliners* story. Joyce could
have cited *The Lake* as a novel whose technique in some ways
resembled that of *Ulysses*, and whose growth from short story to
novel paralleled that of his own book; failing that, one might expect
that as he was lavishing praise on Edouard Dujardin for pioneering
interior monologue in *Les lauriers sont coupés* he could have called
attention to Moore's gracious dedication of *The Lake* to Dujardin,
and to the two men's long friendship, as one reason for his own
interest in Dujardin. Instead, Joyce ignored Moore as much as
possible. The treatment of Moore in *Ulysses* suggests a personal
reason for this odd attitude, for in *Ulysses* Moore, who never
appears in person, gives a party to which Mulligan and most of the
young literary talents in Dublin are invited, while Stephen Dedalus
is pointedly excluded. Joyce had never forgiven Moore for failing to
invite him to his get-togethers at 4 Upper Ely Place, or for Moore's
comments on him that had inevitably reached his ears. In *Ulysses*
Stephen uses his weapon of silence against Moore, refusing to
comment on him while other characters satirize Moore in various
ways: an unidentified character recalls Susan Mitchell's joke about
Moore being Martyn's wild oats (U, 192); John Eglinton and
Mulligan poke fun at the older man's tendency to interlace his
speech with French phrases (U, 211, 214, 405); and the narrator of
the 'Oxen of the Sun' episode calls attention in an absurd manner to
Moore's conversion from 'a papish' to 'a good Williamite' (U, 397).

Joyce and Moore finally met, for the first time, in 1929, a quarter
century after the events of *Ulysses* are supposed to have occurred
and seven years after the publication of the book. The meeting was
cordial, as Moore reported to John Eglinton:

[Joyce] was distinguished, courteous, respectful, and I was the same; he
seemed anxious to accord me the first place. . . This morning he sent me a
book, and pleaded that I had promised to accept a copy of the French
translation of *Ulysses*. I was conquered.[48]

Moore's reaction to *Ulysses* was, however, mixed: although he
thought it better than *Lady Chatterly's Lover* and had been told by a

friend that the book was magnificent, he worried (while claiming not to care one way or the other) that it might be better than *The Brook Kerith*.[49] Writing to Joyce about the book, in September 1929, he found 'the French . . . wilfully exaggerated in places'; a month later he expressed unspecified doubts about 'the inner monologue'. Seven months later, those doubts had been extended to include Dujardin's *Les lauriers sont coupés*, for which Moore now refused to write an introduction:

Now about Dujardin . . . I may live for a few more years, and if I do I shall naturally devote them to my own work. Moreover, I know nothing of the question which apparently agitates France, the discovery of the monologue interieure [*sic*]. In England we don't believe that any discovery has been made. We think, rightly or wrongly, that the monologue interieure existed from time immemorial.[50]

Moore might have thought that Joyce was poking fun at him by sending him the French translation; perhaps Joyce was thinking of the French dedication of *The Lake*, Moore's tendency to drop French phrases, or even the story that on his return to Mayo after years abroad Moore briefly pretended not to be able to converse fluently in English anymore. By May 1931, Moore was apparently annoyed at this standing joke, and Joyce dropped his plan to send Moore the French translation of *Anna Livia Plurabelle* after receiving 'a most furious letter from G.M'.[51] The refusal to write the introduction for Dujardin, and the criticism of the *monologue intérieur*, are evidence of a deeper wound, for despite an intimate friendship with Moore that began in the 1880s Dujardin owed the resuscitation of his literary career to Joyce's statement that he derived the idea for his use of *monologue intérieur* from Dujardin. Moore's letters to Dujardin in the 1920s are strangely silent on the subject of *Ulysses*, and his refusal to read the book until 1929 was probably due in some degree to the way Joyce had usurped his place with Dujardin. After 1922, near the end of his career, when he had long since found his mature style and had written his best novels, Moore was hearing that there was a modern way of describing consciousness, and that the method had been before him all the time in the novel of his old friend Dujardin. What better way of protecting himself than by claiming that *le monologue intérieur* was hardly Dujardin's discovery, much less Joyce's, but was something that had 'existed from time immemorial' – something Moore himself might have used if he had really wanted to?

Such defensive ploys appear throughout the relationship of Moore and Joyce, as each man used his response to the other to manoeuvre his rival into a weaker position. Having ignored Joyce in Ireland, Moore viewed with consternation Joyce's increasing fame in the literary world, never quite understanding the success of this interloper from Dublin. In 1922, while visiting Paris, he saw a man with a black patch over one eye enter the restaurant; fascinated, 'Moore stared at him, and then enquired in a stage whisper if "that" was Joyce, and how he made his living'.[52] Joyce, meanwhile, often dispraised works by Moore that influenced his own work, particularly *The Untilled Field* and *The Lake*; it was one thing to praise *Vain Fortune*, a novel others had ignored, just as he was later to claim Dujardin and Vico as major sources for his works, but it was important that he disparage the books in which Moore hurdled barriers that Joyce feared he might never scale. By the late Twenties, the situation was quite different: with his reputation secure, Joyce could afford to be generous to Moore, even – if we accept the most positive interpretation of his idea – to try to share the Dujardin-related publicity with Moore by having him write the introduction to *Les lauriers sont coupés*. When Moore died, Joyce instructed Harriet Weaver to send to the funeral an ivy-free wreath with the inscription 'To George Moore from James Joyce', then filled his letters of the next two months with bitter references to the failure of the newspapers to mention his gift.[53] It was as if in the end he felt the need to acknowledge publicly a debt that he had long owed, but could only then admit.

NOTES

1   Robert M. Adams, *James Joyce: Common Sense and Beyond* (New York: Random House, 1966), p. 160; Anthony Farrow, *George Moore* (Boston: Twayne Publishers, 1978), p. 129.
2   'Gas from a Burner', in *The Critical Writings of James Joyce*, ed. Ellsworth Mason and Richard Ellmann (New York: Viking Press, 1964), p. 243.
3   Richard Ellmann, *James Joyce* (New York: Oxford University Press, 1959), p. 543.
4   Stanislaus Joyce, *My Brother's Keeper: James Joyce's Early Years*, ed. Richard Ellmann (New York: Viking Press, 1969), pp. 98–99.
5   Graham Hough, 'George Moore and the Nineties', in *Edwardians and Late Victorians: English Institute Essays*, ed. Richard Ellmann (New York: Columbia University Press, 1960), p. 24.
6   Letter from George Russell to W. B. Yeats in *The Letters of James Joyce*, ed. Stuart Gilbert (Vol. I) and Richard Ellmann (Vols. II and III) (New York: Viking Press, 1966), II, 12.
7   *Critical Writings*, p. 69.
8   *Confessions of a Young Man* (London: William Heinemann, 1926), p. 100.

9 'Ireland, Island of Saints and Sages', in *Critical Writings*, p. 171; cf. p. 71, where 'Mr. Moore is really struggling in the backwash of that tide which has advanced from Flaubert through Jakobsen to D'Annunzio'.

10 Frank Budgen, *James Joyce and the Making of Ulysses* (Bloomington: Indiana University Press, 1960), p. 180.

11 *Critical Writings*, p. 71; Ellmann, p. 631. Ellmann also cites Moore's half-serious remark that *Ulysses* 'cannot be a novel, for there isn't a tree in it'.

12 Arthur Power, *Conversations with James Joyce*, ed. Clive Hart (New York: Barnes & Noble, 1974), p. 59; Ellmann, pp. 543–44.

13 Ellmann, p. 418.

14 *Letters of James Joyce*, II, 111.

15 *Letters of James Joyce*, II, 71.

16 *The Untilled Field* (London: T. Fisher Unwin, 1903). The scene with the train schedule follows two pages later, which suggests that these passages came to mind because Joyce had recently read, or reread, the story.

17 Herbert Howarth, *The Irish Writers 1880–1940* (London: Rockliff, 1958), p. 250.

18 Quoted by Marvin Magalaner and Richard M. Kain, *Joyce: The Man, the Work, the Reputation* (New York: Collier Books, 1962), p. 35.

19 *Letters of James Joyce*, II, 134.

20 Janet Egleson Dunleavy, *George Moore: The Artist's Vision, the Storyteller's Art* (Lewisburg: Bucknell University Press, 1973), pp. 120–21.

21 T. R. Henn, cited by Richard Allen Cave in his Afterword to *The Lake* (Gerrards Cross: Colin Smythe, 1980), pp. 208–209.

22 'A Little Cloud', in *Dubliners*, ed. Robert Scholes and A. Walton Litz, Viking Critical Library edition (New York: Penguin Books, 1979).

23 Sister Eileen Kennedy, 'Moore's *Untilled Field* and Joyce's *Dubliners*', *Eire-Ireland* 5, No. 3 (Fall 1970): 81–89, especially 83–86.

24 Patricia Ann McFate, 'Gabriel Conroy and Ned Carmady: A Tale of Two Irish Geese', *College Literature* 5 (1978): 133–38.

25 See especially Michael West, 'George Moore and the Hermeneutics of Joyce's *Dubliners*', *Harvard Library Bulletin* 26 (April 1978): 212–35.

26 Deborah M. Averill, *The Irish Short Story from George Moore to Frank O'Connor* (Washington, D. C.: University Press of America, 1982), pp. 32–33, 48.

27 *George Moore in Transition: Letters to T. Fisher Unwin and Lena Milman, 1894–1910*, ed. Helmut E. Gerber (Detroit: Wayne State University Press, 1968), pp. 246, 247.

28 Ellmann, pp. 259–60.

29 *George Moore in Transition*, p. 245.

30 *Vain Fortune* (New York: Charles Scribner's Sons, 1892), p. 249.

31 Anita Gandolfo, 'A Portrait of the Artist as Critic: Joyce, Moore, and the Background of "The Dead" ', *English Literature in Transition* 22 (1979): 239–50, especially 244–48. Gandolfo traces 'I think he died for me' to passages in 'Mildred Lawson' but does not notice the existence of a similar phrase in *Vain Fortune*.

32 McFate, p. 136.

33 *The Lake* (London: William Heinemann, 1905), p. 303. The same phrase is repeated in the revised edition (1921), reprinted by Colin Smythe, Ltd. (1980), p. 161.

34 *Letters of James Joyce*, II, 154, 157–58.

35 *Letters of James Joyce*, II, 162–63.

36　Ezra Pound, 'James Joyce et Pécuchet', in *Pound/Joyce*, ed. Forrest Read (New York: New Directions, 1967), p. 209. Pound's antipathy to Moore is also evident in his 1914 essay 'A Curious History', which concludes with the statement that 'Mr Moore has succeeded in falling below even his usual level of mendacious pusillanimity' (p. 24).

37　The most thorough discussion of Joyce's use of impressionistic methods in the *Portrait* is by Maurice Beebe: 'The *Portrait* as Portrait: Joyce and Impressionism', *Irish Renaissance Annual* 1 (1980): 13–31.

38　*Stephen Hero*, ed. Theodore Spencer, John J. Slocum, and Herbert Cahoon (New York: New Directions, 1963), p. 28.

39　*A Portrait of the Artist as a Young Man*, ed. Chester G. Anderson, Viking Critical Library edition (New York: Viking Press, 1968).

40　Ellmann, p. 131, notes that Joyce bought Dujardin's book knowing that Dujardin was Moore's friend.

41　Linda Bennett, 'George Moore and James Joyce: Story-teller Versus Stylist', *Studies: An Irish Quarterly Review* 66 (1977): 279; cf. Farrow, p. 125.

42　Richard Allen Cave, *A Study of the Novels of George Moore* (Gerrards Cross: Colin Smythe, New York: Barnes & Noble, 1978), p. 192.

43　Ellmann, p. 243.

44　Bennett, p. 279.

45　*Ulysses* (New York: Modern Library, 1961).

46　J. B. Lyons cites Gogarty's letter of 18 November 1905 to G. K. A. Bell: '[Moore] owes me gratitude if such a thing were ever his, for forbearing to proceed against him for a libel in that book of his. As long as my mother does not hear of it I don't care about Moore's audacious act. All he wants, I know, is to make me angry and by my kicking up a row advertise it. I told him I rejoiced that he had cast the ring for me: one can only die once, and, as I am yet alive in spite of the oblivion he has provided, my name must now do something – it cannot die again!' *Oliver St. John Gogarty: The Man of Many Talents* (Dublin: Blackwater Press, 1980), p. 322.

47　Albert J. Solomon, 'A Moore in *Ulysses*', *James Joyce Quarterly* 10 (Winter 1973): 218–19. Solomon quotes the description of the incident from Ulick O'Connor's biography of Gogarty.

48　*Letters of George Moore*, ed. John Eglinton (Bournemouth: Sydenham & Co., 1942), p. 84.

49　Geraint Goodwin, *Conversations with George Moore* (New York: Alfred A. Knopf, 1930), pp. 164–65.

50　*Letters of James Joyce*, III, 194, 195, 197.

51　*Letters of James Joyce*, I, 304.

52　Joseph Hone, *The Life of George Moore* (London: Victor Gollancz, 1936), p. 376. Ellmann, p. 544, also reports Moore's concern with the source of Joyce's income.

53　*Letters of James Joyce*, I, 333–36.

GEORGE MOORE AND SAMUEL BECKETT: CROSS CURRENTS AND CORRESPONDENCES

MELVIN J. FRIEDMAN

George Moore and Samuel Beckett, despite their Irish backgrounds and Joycean entanglements, would seem to have little in common. Beckett's increasingly spare and accentless prose could not be less like Moore's verbal exuberance. Beckett has always honoured Paul Verlaine's famous line from his 'Art poétique': 'Prends l'éloquence et tords-lui son cou!'; Moore also respected Verlaine – he remarked in his *Confessions of a Young Man*, 'Verlaine became my poet' – but would probably have preferred another sequence from the same poem: 'Oh! la nuance seule fiance/Le rêve au rêve et la flûte au cor!' Beckett's mature work seems to occupy the outer edges of postmodernism while Moore comfortably enjoys the less daring and less experimental securities of modernism. The deadening, stillborn silences of Beckett's recent texts point to the failure of language and storytelling while Moore's lush and enthusiastic cadences offer a nineteenth-century assurance that all is well with the literary enterprise. While Beckett offers cries of despair in his belief that 'expression is an impossible act' Moore allows his 'nonsense thoughts' full play.

Critics have found sources for Beckett's work in every corner of literary and philosophic endeavour: from the Greek dramatists through Proust, Joyce, and Kafka; from the pre-Socratics through Wittgenstein and Fritz Mauthner.[1] George Moore's name rarely surfaces and then only casually. Sighle Kennedy offers the intriguing suggestion that Murphy's last will, spelling out the conditions of the unorthodox disposal of his ashes, 'owes some of its rampancy to Beckett's memory of what Gogarty termed "George Moore's Ultimate Joke" '.[2] Kennedy's text is an essay by Oliver St. John Gogarty that mockingly describes the circumstances of Moore's funeral which 'the principal intended ... to be an embarrassing jest'.[3] Gogarty offers a sentence from Moore's will, disconcertingly read aloud by the deceased writer's brother, Maurice, 'my body to be cremated and my ashes spread over Hampstead Heath where the donkeys graze' (p.28) and then playfully suggests, 'He [Moore] knew quite well that his family would never permit his ashes to be scattered among the donkeys. The newspapers would be full of the scandal. No. Ashes to asses would never do' (p.29). The Beckett of *Murphy*, whose gospel began 'in the beginning was the pun', would certainly have responded to these words and enjoyed the eccentric behaviour, if he knew about them. Deirdre Bair nowhere mentions Moore in her *Samuel Beckett: A Biography*, but that is no reason to discount Kennedy's tantalizing suggestion.

Richard Allen Cave sees Beckett's television play *Eh Joe* 'as another imaginative redeployment' (along with Joyce's 'The Dead') of Moore's *Vain Fortune*.[4] He convincingly juxtaposes Beckett's Joe with Joyce's Gabriel Conroy and Moore's Hubert Price. Cave does stop short of insisting that *Vain Fortune* actually influenced *Eh Joe* by falling back on the verbal formula, 'it is tempting to see'.

Anthony Farrow, author of the Twayne book on George Moore, wrote a Cornell Ph. D. dissertation entitled 'Currents in the Irish Novel: George Moore, James Joyce, Samuel Beckett'. The dissertation abstract begins: 'This study of the three most important Irish novelists of the last hundred years is intended to define certain continuities which have persisted in these writers throughout all the changes wrought by time and shifting literary allegiances'. Farrow goes on to say: 'Many of Beckett's qualities as a novelist are specifically traceable to the examples of Moore and Joyce'.[5]

Kennedy, Cave, and Farrow all suggest affinities rather than influences. They place intermediary Irish presences between Beckett and Moore: Gogarty on one occasion, Joyce on the other two. These are cautionary first steps, responsibly taken. The absence of clear evidence linking Beckett with Moore – despite Richard Cave's surprisingly assured but undocumented 'given Samuel Beckett's known interest in Moore's work' (p.131) – makes one fall back on the vague language of analogies and rapprochements.

Beckett, who has always shown exemplary restraint when asked to discuss the sources for his work, did indicate in a letter to S. E. Gontarski, dated June 16, 1982, that he admired Moore and that he recently reread *Celibate Lives*. He apparently often returns to *Hail and Farewell* and has enjoyed *Conversations in Ebury Street*. Nancy Cunard, the author of *GM: Memories of George Moore* and publisher of both Moore and Beckett at the Hours Press, often spoke to the younger writer about the older one.[6] One can scarcely speak of influence with this letter as one's text! We know from Deirdre Bair's biography and elsewhere that Beckett met Nancy

Cunard during his Paris years at the École Normale Supérieure and that she published his 'Whoroscope' and 'From the Only Poet to a Shining Whore (For Henry Crowder to Sing)', both in 1930. Although during this period Nancy Cunard may have brought Beckett to Moore's work, there is no indication that she ever brought Beckett to Moore. (Bair's biography is corroborated by the fact that Beckett's name does not appear a single time in *GM: Memories of George Moore*.) Alas that literary history was thus deprived of another fabled meeting, like the one involving Proust and Joyce in Paris in May, 1921, with its many versions. Without documentary evidence of a stronger connection between the two writers, however, we are left with the intriguing suggestions of Kennedy, Cave, and Farrow – and with what we ourselves can glean from cross currents and correspondences.

II

Impressionism, of course, is the method of deriving meaning from cross currents and correspondences. An impressionistic method has a certain appropriateness when dealing with writers who were also formidable critics; Beckett who began his career by confronting difficult texts by Joyce and Proust; and Moore who never stopped explaining the intricacies of the French Symbolist poets, the French Impressionists, and Wagner to his English and Irish readers. The kind of criticism these two Irishmen wrote has a strong intuitive and impressionistic flavour, the kind preferred by their adopted homeland, France, a country which has nurtured novelists and poets who were also critics of the arts. From Diderot's *Salons*, through Baudelaire's *Curiosités Esthétiques*, to Malraux's *Les Voix du silence* and *La Métamorphose des dieux*, French writers have been spirited observers of painting. Baudelaire and Dujardin (one of Moore's closest friends) were committed Wagnerians and their fellow Symbolist Verlaine started his 'Art poétique' with the line 'De la musique avant toute chose'. The French climate was then entirely suitable for these two Irishmen *manqué* who were not only critics of literature but of the other art forms.

Formal criticism occupies only a tiny corner of Beckett's *oeuvre*. His first publication, 'Dante . . . Bruno. Vico . . . Joyce', was the opening contribution to a symposium on Joyce, which carried the preposterous title, *Our Exagmination Round His Factification For Incamination of Work in Progress* (1929). This 6000 word essay was followed two years later by a 72-page monograph, *Proust*. Beckett published some half-dozen book reviews, between 1934 and 1938, in *The Criterion*, *The Bookman*, *Dublin Magazine*, and *Transition*, and returned briefly to literary journalism with a brief piece on his friend Thomas McGreevy's *Jack B. Yeats* in the August 4, 1945 *Irish Times*. The discussion of Yeats's painting in this review seemed to prepare for the art criticism Beckett was to write intermittently during the next decade, especially on the work of Bram and Geer van Velde. If all this scattered material were to be collected in a single volume it would not run as long as any one of Moore's critical gatherings, like *Modern Painting* or *Impressions and Opinions*. Despite the occasional nature of Beckett's criticism it is an essential enough part of his canon to have attracted a good deal of attention, including a forty-page section of Lawrence Harvey's *Samuel Beckett: Poet and Critic*.

Harvey insists on the impressionistic nature of Beckett's critical enterprise. Beckett has always been unhappy with exegetical and evaluative critics who torture the work of art by their insistent probings and dissections – to the point where he coined his famous expletive in *Waiting for Godot*, 'Crritic!' Beckett agrees with Baudelaire in feeling that the creative temperament is far better suited to critical response than the professional exegete. Harvey ends up characterizing Beckett's criticism as 're-creation'. At its most successful 'it approaches the nature of art itself'.[7]

The cornerstone of Beckett's achievement as a critic is *Proust*. It is of crucial importance to every critic of *À la recherche du temps perdu*, even now more than fifty years after it was written. (It has a certain timeliness at the moment in the wake of the new English version of Proust's novel which appeared in 1981, based on the 1954 corrected French text in the Pléiade series: Beckett, in his foreword, lamented 'the abominable edition of the *Nouvelle Revue Française*, in sixteen volumes,' which was all that was available to him in 1931.) Its discussion of memory, habit, time, death, and mystical experiences in Proust's work is as subtle and judicious as any we have, partly because of its proximity to, what Harvey calls, 'the nature of art itself'. Beckett does not dissect; he re-creates through images and juxtapositions. He sees the literary enterprise as akin to the plastic and musical arts, much like George Moore. He mentions Proust's impressionism and insists that 'For Proust, as for the painter, style is more a question of vision than of technique'.[8] He speaks in Wagnerian terms of the 'Leitmotiv of his composition' (p.22) and later on strongly asserts that 'Music is the catalytic element in the work of Proust' (p.71).

Certain sentiments expressed in the Proust monograph would

probably have delighted Moore if he had known about them; Moore was always proclaiming the kinship literature had with the other arts. Thus in his chapter on Degas in *Modern Painting* we have these juxtapositions: 'Baudelaire was the only poet who ever did this; Degas is the only painter'; '. . . like Wagner, Degas is possessed of such intuitive knowledge of the qualities inherent in the various elements nature presents that he is enabled, after having disintegrated, to re-integrate them, and with surety of always finding a new and more elegant synthesis'.[9] These remarks have much the same impressionistic ring as those we find in Beckett's *Proust* – in the way they cross over so naturally from one art form to another. It is a critical *donnée* of both Moore and Beckett that the arts never fail to interact and the most judicious way of viewing them is through their points of convergence.

While Moore's views of literature and the arts seem akin to Beckett's (at least those Beckett expressed in the 1930s), the older writer could scarcely share the younger one's enthusiasm for Proust. Nancy Cunard reports on Moore's distaste for Proust's style: ' "He writes like a man trying to plough a field with a pair of knitting needles!" '[10] Although he admitted the importance of the author of *À la recherche du temps perdu*, Moore 'found no pleasure in reading twenty, thirty pages about something that might have been fully expressed in one, in two' (pp.154–155). Of course, Moore always thought of himself as uniquely tuned into the niceties of French style; he keenly felt Proust's 'betrayal' of a language which seemed nurtured on clarity and compression. Beckett expressed a quite different notion in his *Proust*: 'It is a tiring style, but it does not tire the mind. The clarity of the phrase is cumulative and explosive . . . The complaint that it is an involved style, full of periphrasis, obscure and impossible to follow, has no foundation whatsoever' (p.68).

If Beckett and Moore had ever had the occasion to discuss a writer they both knew personally, like James Joyce, they would surely have had their differences. Many critics have discussed Moore's views of Joyce, including Patrick McCarthy in the present volume, and have pointed to ambivalent responses and characteristic epigrammatic dismissals, such as Moore's famous remark about *Ulysses* made to Janet Flanner: 'It cannot be a novel, for there isn't a tree in it!' (quoted in *GM: Memories of George Moore*, p.162). Beckett, who began his career in the shadow of Joyce, would probably not have been amused by this tongue-in-cheek irreverence. The young Beckett, writing about 'Work in Progress', was quick to rise to his mentor's defense:

Here is direct expression – pages and pages of it. And if you don't understand it, Ladies and Gentlemen, it is because you are too decadent to receive it. You are not satisfied unless form is so strictly divorced from content that you can comprehend the one almost without bothering to read the other.[11]

Of course, when commenting on these quite different responses to Proust and Joyce, we should keep in mind that Moore was sixty-one when the first volume of *A la recherche du temps perdu* appeared and seventy when *Ulysses* was published, while Beckett responded to these writers while still in his mid-twenties. Moore was confronting young upstarts, many years his junior, obscenely disfiguring the novel of his beloved Balzac, while Beckett looked to Proust and Joyce as bold experimenters who were enlarging the possibilities of fiction to help accommodate his own future displacements and fragmentations of narrative. The younger Moore, who proclaimed the virtues of Manet, Wagner, and the Symbolists, was as stubbornly resistant to the established ways of producing and viewing art in the 1880s and 1890s as Beckett was in the 1930s. And that is important to remember. They both had a sure sense of what mattered in the avant-garde and what was most likely to survive.

As critics, then, Moore and Beckett have a great deal in common. They use rather similar impressionistic responses to record their appreciation for the genuine in the work of their contemporaries. They are both immensely well read and call upon their awareness of tradition at every turn. Beckett's Proust is seen as having much to do with Schopenhauer, Dostoevsky, and Calderón, as well as a variety of French thinkers and writers. His Joyce profits from deep awareness of Italian literature and thought from Dante through Bruno to Vico. George Moore also roams with ease across the European continent, returning to early periods at will, in the course of assessing the artists and writers who mattered to him.

Beckett started out by writing fiction and poetry with one hand, criticism with the other. In his early work the functions never remained entirely separate. His still-unpublished first novel, *Dream of Fair to Middling Women*, contains a great deal of literary reference, especially in conversations. The amount diminishes and becomes more oblique in his 1934 collection of stories, *More Pricks Than Kicks*; for example, this reference to Rousseau's *Confessions*: ' "Can it be possible that you passed through Chambéry and never called on Mme de Warens?" ' or this pastiched reminder of the end of Joyce's 'The Dead': '. . . and the rain fell in a uniform untroubled manner. It fell upon the bay, the littoral, the mountains and the plains, and notably upon the Central Bog it fell with a rather desolate uniformity'.[12] He virtually made an art form of oblique reference in *Murphy*, as every variety of allusion weaves its way through the text, often undermining the role of the narrator and undercutting the integrity of the narrative. 'Blooming buzzing confusion', for example, are words from William James wrenched out of context; ' "Since Heaven lay about you as a bedwetter" ' offers a redoing of a famous line of Wordsworth.[13] These and many other echoes and distortions have the effect of disrupting the telling.

The disruptions are of a different sort in the more mature fiction and the references to other writers and works begin to disappear, although never entirely. One can read along in one of the brief texts, which Beckett has been writing for the past two decades, and suddenly come upon '. . . wrung from Dante one of his rare wan smiles'.[14] But the habit has been vastly curtailed as language and narrative have increasingly worn down. Beckett stopped writing criticism per se a long time ago and his fiction has almost wholly disentangled itself from an allusive, critical function.

With Moore, criticism and fiction have always proceeded hand in hand. The characters in his novels and stories freely discuss literature and the arts with quite the same tone and authority as Moore does himself in *Confessions of a Young Man*, *Hail and Farewell*, and *Conversations in Ebury Street*. Moore apparently saw no generic differences between fact and fable and so blurred many distinctions between the two. He is more unconventional in essayistic works like *Hail and Farewell* and *Conversations in Ebury Street* than he is in *The Lake*, *Vain Fortune*, or *Celibate Lives*, despite the fact that he was writing fiction during a period of elaborate experimentation for the novel. A number of critics, like Richard Cave and William Blissett,[15] have convincingly studied the strong Wagnerian elements in Moore, but these musical intrusions do not really add up to innovation of the kind that the later James, Conrad, Proust, and Joyce were pursuing in altering the shape and narrative foundations of the novel. While writing autobiography and related forms Moore permitted himself liberties of invention and improvisation which he indulged in less strenuously in the fiction. It is true, as Janet Dunleavy points out, that 'pattern and rhythm sometimes reminiscent of French idiom characterize the prose of Moore's last novels',[16] but this is really further evidence, on the one hand, of the comfortable modernism which carries through the fiction. The experimental risks of a work like *Hail and Farewell*, on the other hand, may explain why someone like Samuel Beckett often returns to it (as he reported to Gontarski).

Indeed, as several critics have suggested, *Hail and Farewell* is very like a novel – just as one of its forerunners, Rousseau's *Confessions*, surely is. It probably stands to his career as *The Confessions* does to that of the 18th century Genevan. I mention Rousseau's autobiography because it is one of those French texts which Moore devotedly fondled and which he referred to several times in the 'Ave' section of *Hail and Farewell*.

Hail and Farewell, on the surface, is the testimonial to Moore's triumphant return to Ireland as he volunteered himself for unlimited literary service in the Gaelic Revival.[17] It is mainly, however, an immense *cri de conscience*, with a babel of voices breaking in to disrupt the telling. It is a hybrid work which combines story with criticism with travelogue with confession. Moore even throws in several pages of French dialogue he wrote, with the characteristic Moorean afterthought: '. . . if not in French, in a language comprehensible to a Frenchman'.[18] The French are, of course, very much on his mind during this return-to-Ireland autobiography and their presence occasionally recalls to him those two copying clerks from Flaubert's unfinished novel, Bouvard and Pécuchet – the 19th century Don Quixote and Sancho Panza who, incidentally, seemed to be the models for Beckett's 'pseudocouple', Mercier and Camier.[19]

Hail and Farewell is an open-ended work in which everything seems allowable. A narrator, George Moore, permits himself eccentric divagations, wild dislocations of chronology; imaginary conversations mingle with authentic dialogue.[20] Moore seems to delight in the outrageousness of his remarks to Edward Martyn and to his brother Maurice (the Colonel) – which go on often for pages – on the many disadvantages of the Roman Catholic Church and on the failure of any Catholic since the Reformation to write a book that matters. Just as he enjoys running down the religion of his ancestors, he takes great pleasure in speaking ill of their language:

My indifference to English poetry extended to the language itself; English seemed to me to lack consistency that evening – a woolly language without a verbal system or agreement between the adjectives and nouns. So did I rave until, wearied of finding fault with everything English, my thoughts melted away into memories of the French poets (p. 223).

It is clear from *Hail and Farewell* that Moore appreciates the paradox of returning to a country whose religion and language he doesn't approve of; of urging on its literary inhabitants the use of another language, Irish ('the grand old tongue'), which he doesn't know himself; of spreading the gospel of French art and literature while supposedly championing the cause of a renaissance in Ireland. And the note which Moore sounds early in the 'Ave', 'Far more true would it be to say that an Irishman must fly from Ireland if he would be himself', (p.56) accompanies him through the entire awkward enterprise.

The Protestant Samuel Beckett, who kept leaving Dublin for France, Germany, and England during restless *Wanderjahre* and ended up settling permanently in Paris, seems to be cut from the same literary cloth as the author of *Hail and Farewell*. It is remarkable that even Moore's geographical terrain is the same as Beckett's. France, Germany, and England offered both writers alternatives, at various stages of their lives, to a country which Moore could think of only as foreign: 'Ireland and I have ever been strangers, without an idea in common'. (*Hail and Farewell*, p.77) France was the temptress – early for Moore, early and late for Beckett – and its language, literature, and art never ceased to engage their affections. Beckett, of course, made French the original language of many of his most important works of fiction and drama; Moore wrote in it occasionally, but never felt comfortable enough with it to write anything more sustained than the thirty-page chapter 4 of *Conversations in Ebury Street*. Germany served as something of a vacation land for both. Moore made the pilgrimage to Bayreuth, which he described so elegantly in *Hail and Farewell*, with Edward Martyn to accommodate his enthusiasm for Wagner. Beckett as a young man courted his cousin Peggy Sinclair in Kassel and has been going to Berlin in recent years to direct German translations of his plays. London offered Beckett a temporary refuge from Dublin after he decided to leave his teaching post at Trinity College. Moore spent his final years holding court on Ebury Street, London. The cultures and landscapes of these countries mattered a great deal to these two writers. In a certain sense, they both (especially Beckett) belong as much to the Continent as they do to Ireland.

III

These two Irishmen, who belong to different generations but whose careers touched briefly (though indirectly) and whose sensibilities seem to have much in common, converge occasionally in their fiction. Moore entitled two of his collections of short fiction *Celibates* and *Celibate Lives*. The men and women who give their names to the stories in these volumes have what can be called a 'devotion to the single life'.[21] It is not so much that Moore's celibates either avoid or fail to enter into the married state as that they seem positively devoted to their solitariness, to cultivating their loneliness. Some, like Wilfrid Holmes and Albert Nobbs in *Celibate Lives*, live eccentrically and desperately alone; others, like Sarah Gwynn in *Celibate Lives* and Agnes Lahens in *Celibates*, try living in the world but function best in convents; still others, like Mildred Lawson in *Celibates* and Henrietta Marr in *Celibate Lives*, flirt endlessly with the temptations of cultivated society, of the art world, and of male companionship, but end up in frustration (in Henrietta's case, suicide).[22]

These unmarried and sometimes even unmarriageable characters seem to belong to a separate species – of Moore's invention. They have a marked talent for failing to accommodate, to adjust. There is a passage in Hermann Hesse's preface to *Steppenwolf*, in which the author describes his protagonist, Harry Haller, that comes very close to explaining the type of the celibate:

I saw that Haller was a genius of suffering and that in the meaning of many sayings of Nietzsche, he had created within himself an ingenious, a boundless and frightful capacity for pain. I saw at the same time that the root of his pessimism was not world-contempt but self-contempt; for however mercilessly he might annihilate institutions and persons in his talk he never spared himself.[23]

Steppenwolf, curiously enough, was first published in 1927, the same year as *Celibate Lives*. The 'magic theater' depicted in Hesse's novel presents a timeless Germany dominated by Goethe and the great German composers, which is not so different from the Germany Moore imagined through much of his literary life.

Closest to the type of Harry Haller is probably Wilfrid Holmes, whose story is the first one in *Celibate Lives*. He is perhaps milder and more self-effacing than Hesse's character but shares with him the intense pain and suffering. He lives his mature years in lonely rooming houses, pursuing his two passions: one for music, the other for uncovering the sources of the Tristan and Isolde legend. We know from the opening words of the story that Wilfrid is not only the youngest of the Holmes children but different from the others, 'all of whom were making their way in the world'.[24] *He* was never to make his way in the world, Moore tells us through indirection in the first few pages; this fact is dramatized through the remainder of this bleak tale. Wilfrid's surrogate life in art, with his unfinished opera and vain search for the origins of the Tristan and Isolde legend, offers an existence with numerous frustrations. The choice of the great love legend as his special subject is ironical as Wilfrid never experiences love. He is probably the purest of all Moore's celibates: marriage is not even a possibility for him.

Samuel Beckett's fictional creatures, from Murphy through the Unnamable, seem to have something in common with Moore's celibates. (Beckett might have had an eerie sense of 'reading the book of himself'[25] when he recently reread *Celibate Lives*.) Moore's stories are, of course, more conventionally fleshed out, more intricately plotted. When one approaches Beckett's derelict types, beginning with the 'seedy solipsist' Murphy who dies unpleasantly in his garret at the insane asylum where he works, one gets a privileged glance at failure,[26] perhaps a more desperate kind than Moore knew about. In fact, one might say that Wilfrid Holmes, Albert Nobbs, and those other celibates offer a heady dose of *fin de siècle* and early 20th century self-contempt and pessimism which never quite reaches the proportions of Murphy's, Watt's, and Molloy's alienation. The difference is more a matter of degree than of kind. Beckett's generation is probably more receptive to the extremes of maladjustment and failure than was Moore's.

Moore's characters often relieve their solitariness and despair through their involvement in the arts. Wilfrid Holmes keeps working at his opera and playing his flute. Mildred Lawson and Henrietta Marr are painters. John Norton works on a book about monks and bishops who wrote in Latin early in the Christian era and once offers this characteristically 'celibate' response: ' "People don't interest me. I am interested in things much more than in people – in pictures, in music, in sculpture" '.[27]

These celibates often engage in lengthy and knowing conversations about the arts, but none ever quite succeeds as an artist, musician, or writer. Beckett's characters fail even more completely. The narrators of the trilogy, *Molloy*, *Malone Dies*, and *The Unnamable*, all seem to be writers *manqué*. They are always putting pen to paper, turning out reports, telling stories – exercises in failure. The most versatile storyteller of the group, Malone, goes into the frustrations of the writer's craft in detail: 'I did not want to write, but I had to resign myself to it in the end. It is in order to know where I have got to, where he has got to. At first I did not write, I just said the thing. Then I forgot what I had said'.[28] Malone even has difficulty keeping track of his writing instrument: 'What a misfortune, the pencil must have slipped from my fingers, for I have only just succeeded in recovering it after forty-eight hours (see above) of intermittent efforts' (p. 222).

The ambiguity about sex expressed by the narrators of the trilogy is also something they have in common with certain of Moore's celibates. John Norton, for example, fell in love with a woman whose 'figure is slight even to boyishness' (p.381) and felt that 'the present age, so essentially the age of women, was repellent to him' (p.369). His final desire 'to find escape from the ignominy of life' (p.452) has much to do with his ambiguous notions of sexuality. The distinctions between the sexes blur almost completely in the later story, 'Albert Nobbs'. Albert first appears as a waiter in a Dublin family hotel. It soon turns out that he/she is actually a woman disguised as a man. Albert tells her story to a male house-painter who also turns out to be a woman. (Pronominal confusions are rampant and work hand in hand with artful changes in point of view. Proust, who gave most of his female characters names which could easily have been turned into male names, would have been delighted with the sexual ambiguities which are at work in Moore's story.) There is a certain surreal quality in 'Albert Nobbs' which, together with the tone of desperation, makes one think of the bleak, *outre-tombe* landscapes of Beckett's trilogy.

There is a lighter side to Moore and Beckett. Both have developed senses of the comic and incongruous, which perhaps reflects on their Irish inheritance. Two scenes, one from the second part of Beckett's *Molloy*, the other from Moore's *The Lake*, have certain parallels. Both have to do with religious hypocrisy. Ritual and cant appear to triumph over sincere belief in both instances. In the Beckett scene, Moran, the narrator of part two of *Molloy*, fails to attend mass on a Sunday morning because of an unexpected visit. To compensate, he schedules a private communion with his priest. As he prepares for the visit, the following thoughts go through his mind:

> I remembered with annoyance the lager I had just absorbed. Would I be granted the body of Christ after a pint of Wallenstein? And if I said nothing? Have you come fasting, my son? He would not ask. But God would know, sooner or later. Perhaps he would pardon me. But would the eucharist produce the same effect, taken on top of beer, however light? I could always try. What was the teaching of the Church on the matter? What if I were about to commit sacrilege? I decided to suck a few peppermints on the way to the presbytery.[29]

These hypocritical concerns carry through the actual encounter with the priest, a moment of religious satire worthy of Molière or Voltaire.

The scene in *The Lake*, which occurs toward the end of the novel, involves the baptism of a child who has a Protestant grandmother and a Catholic grandmother. The Protestant grandmother, Mrs.

Rean, manages to make off with the infant in a very unChristian manner, according to the description offered by the other grandmother to her priest:

'Your reverence had only just turned in the chapel gate when Mrs. Rean ran from behind the hedge, and, getting in front of me who was going to the chapel with the baby in me arms, she said: "Now, I'll be damned if I'll have that child christened a Catholic"; and didn't she snatch the child and run away, taking a short cut across the fields to the minister's?'[30]

She then asks her priest the following seminal questions:

'Your reverence, will the child be always a Protestant? Hasn't the holy water of the Church more power in it than the water they have? Don't they only throw it at the child?' (p.286)

This encounter reflects the same concern with the appearance of religion at the expense of genuine piety that we found in Beckett. Moore's distaste for the Roman Catholic Church, which occupied so many pages of *Hail and Farewell*, is in evidence here. But there is also his loathing of the entire religious scene with its ceremonial mockeries and superstitions.

Other intriguing points of convergence offer additional evidence that both these creators of bleak types – such as Albert Nobbs, John Norton, and Wilfrid Holmes on the one hand and Watt, Molloy, and Malone on the other – dramatize comic moments with rare dexterity. So although direct influence cannot be established, Moore and Beckett, it finally should be said, thus offer a study not only of surface contrasts but also of deeper and more subtle cross-currents and correspondences.

NOTES

1   Typical of these studies are my 'The Novels of Samuel Beckett: An Amalgam of Joyce and Proust', *Comparative Literature*, 12 (Winter 1960), 47–58 and Ruby Cohn's 'Philosophical Fragments in the Works of Samuel Beckett', *Criticism*, 6 (Winter 1964), 33–43.

2   Sighle Kennedy, *Murphy's Bed: A Study of Real Sources and Sur-Real Associations in Samuel Beckett's First Novel* (Lewisburg: Bucknell University Press, 1971), p. 271.

3   Oliver St. John Gogarty, 'George Moore's Ultimate Joke', in his *Intimations* (New York: Abelard Press, 1950), pp. 25–26; hereafter cited parenthetically in the text.

4   Richard Allen Cave, *A Study of the Novels of George Moore*, Irish Literary Studies 3 (Gerrards Cross: Colin Smythe, 1978), pp. 131–132; hereafter cited parenthetically in the text.

5 *Dissertation Abstracts International*, 33: 5719A–5720A. While I have not seen the dissertation itself, I had occasion to chat with Anthony Farrow on the phone about his doctoral thesis and his notion of the relationship between Beckett and Moore. He sees no direct influence of Moore's work on Beckett but views these writers as 'congenial minds' and notes a striking sense of the comic which they seem to have in common.

6 I am grateful to Professor S. E. Gontarski for showing me this letter and allowing me to refer to its contents.

7 Lawrence E. Harvey, *Samuel Beckett*: *Poet and Critic* (Princeton: Princeton University Press, 1970), pp. 440–441.

8 Samuel Beckett, *Proust* (New York: Grove Press, 1957), p. 67; hereafter cited parenthetically in the text.

9 George Moore, *Modern Painting*, Carra Edition, Vol. 19 (New York: Boni and Liveright, 1923), pp. 252, 253.

10 Nancy Cunard, *GM: Memories of George Moore* (London: Rupert Hart-Davis, 1956), p. 154; hereafter cited parenthetically in the text.

11 Samuel Beckett, 'Dante. . . Bruno. Vico.. Joyce', in *Our Exagmination Round His Factification For Incamination of Work in Progress*, by Samuel Beckett, Marcel Brion, et al (New York: New Directions, 1962), p. 13.

12 Samuel Beckett, *More Pricks Than Kicks* (New York: Grove Press, 1970), pp. 24, 83. Ruby Cohn first pointed out this parody of 'The Dead' in her *Samuel Beckett*: *The Comic Gamut* (New Brunswick: Rutgers University Press, 1962), pp. 33–34.

13 Samuel Beckett, *Murphy* (New York: Grove Press, 1957): 'blooming buzzing confusion' appears twice, on pp.29 and 245; the Wordsworth revision appears on p. 217.

14 Samuel Beckett, *The Lost Ones*, trans. by the author (New York: Grove Press, 1972), p. 14.

15 See chapters 7 and 9 of Cave's *A Study of the Novels of George Moore* and William Blissett's 'George Moore and Literary Wagnerism', *Comparative Literature*, 13 (Winter 1961), 52–71.

16 Janet Egleson Dunleavy, *George Moore: The Artist's Vision, The Storyteller's Art* (Lewisburg: Bucknell University Press, 1973), p. 137.

17 Joyce, of course, caught the presumption and ridiculousness of the gesture in the library scene of *Ulysses*: 'They [Moore and Edward Martyn] remind one of don Quixote and Sancho Panza. Our national epic has yet to be written, Dr Sigerson says. Moore is the man for it. A knight of the rueful countenance here in Dublin. With a saffron kilt? O'Neill Russell? O, yes, he must speak the grand old tongue. And his Dulcinea?' (New York: Random House, 1961), p. 192.

18 George Moore, *Hail and Farewell*: *Ave, Salve, Vale*, ed. Richard Cave (Gerrards Cross: Colin Smythe, 1976), p. 249; hereafter cited parenthetically in the text.

19 See Samuel Beckett's *Mercier and Camier*, trans. by the author (New York: Grove Press, 1974); although finished in 1946, Beckett did not publish the original French version until 1970, his English translation until 1974.

20 Richard Cave offers useful discussions of some of these matters both in his *A Study of the Novels of George Moore* and in his introduction to his edition of *Hail and Farewell*.

21 *The Oxford Dictionary of English Etymology*, ed. C. T. Onions, with the assistance of G. W. S. Friedrichsen and R. W. Burchfield (London: Oxford University Press, 1966), p. 157, offers these words as part of a definition of celibacy.

22 Edwin Gilcher, in his *A Bibliography of George Moore* (DeKalb: Northern Illinois University Press, 1970), p. 51, indicates that the story 'Henrietta Marr' is a rewriting of 'Mildred Lawson'. However, there are sufficient differences, especially in the endings, to merit reading both versions. Moore reworked a number of these 'Celibate' stories over the years; this character type obviously fascinated him through much of his writing career.

23 Hermann Hesse, *Steppenwolf*, trans. Basil Creighton, rev. Walter Sorell (New York: Modern Library, 1963), p. 10.

24 George Moore, 'Wilfrid Holmes', in his *Celibate Lives* (London: William Heinemann, 1927), p. 1.

25 Mallarmé's words about Hamlet, quoted in Joyce's *Ulysses*, p. 187.

26 Failure is an essential word in Beckett's vocabulary. In a 1949 dialogue with Georges Duthuit, Beckett even likened the artistic act to failure: '. . . to be an artist is to fail, as no other dare fail, that failure is his world and the shrink from it desertion, art and craft, good housekeeping, living. No, no, allow me to expire. I know that all that is required now, in order to bring even this horrible matter to an acceptable conclusion, is to make of this submission, this admission, this fidelity to failure, a new occasion . . .' This hymn to failure is found in 'Three Dialogues', in *Samuel Beckett: A Collection of Critical Essays*, ed. Martin Esslin (Englewood Cliffs: Prentice-Hall, 1965), p. 21.

27 George Moore, 'John Norton', in his *Celibates* (London: Walter Scott, 1895), p. 336; hereafter cited parenthetically in the text.

28 Samuel Beckett, *Malone Dies*, trans. by the author, in *Three Novels* (New York: Grove Press, 1965), p. 207; hereafter cited parenthetically in the text.

29 Samuel Beckett, *Molloy*, trans. by the author and Patrick Bowles, in *Three Novels*, p. 97.

30 George Moore, *The Lake* (New York and London: D. Appleton and Co., 1913), p. 285; hereafter cited parenthetically in the text.

COLLECTING MOORE

EDWIN GILCHER

George Moore was not himself a collector, either of his own books or of those of other writers, as A. J. A. Symons learned when he sought Moore's assistance while attempting to assemble material for his projected but never completed *A Bibliography of the Writers & Illustrators of the Eighteen Nineties*. But for anyone attempting to become better acquainted with this unique Anglo-Irish author (and I can assure you that it is a rewarding relationship), collecting his books is a must. Collecting is the secret here, for the most certain route to really knowing GM, as he was called by those closest to him, is through his books – not in just any text that happens to be available, but rather by comparing the many and various texts, tracing his development as a writer, and assimilating the progress of his thought. And that, I can also assure you, is a real challenge.

Writing did not come easily to GM. In fact, he turned author only after coming to the painful realization that he did not have the ability to become a painter. Thereafter his entire writing career of more than fifty years was one of attempting to achieve a more perfect result through seemingly endless revisions and rewritings. Collecting his books in these various versions enables the reader to trace his progression through his multitudinous phases from his earlier 'naturalism' to his later books with their 'melodic line'.

GM approved of this, in fact encouraged it, for according to William Lyon Phelps (*Autobiography With Letters*, New York and London, 1939) Moore said, 'Just as I believe the worst of all sins is bad writing, so I believe the highest virtue is found in corrections, in an author's revision. If you wish to estimate the true value of an author's art, study his revisions.' This I attempted to do, but for a slightly different reason, as I gathered together the textual and other variants to use as source material for my *A Bibliography of George Moore* (Northern Illinois University Press, 1970). Starting while GM was still alive and continuing during a period of more than forty years, I was able to assemble probably the most complete collection of his works ever brought together. It contained not only the sought-after first and limited editions, but also the many revised editions and little known works of rather an ephemeral nature, all required for me to obtain a complete bibliographic picture of GM's writing career.

My collection, now at Arizona State University, fortunately was formed at a time of more moderate prices and during that period when his popularity as a 'collectible' author was at a low ebb. Prices are always relative, and while some may seem to be so inflated as to be almost prohibitive, collectors must remember that this has always been the case. If collectors are not too impetuous and have the patience to wait, most things will come their way, but there are some items that should be grasped at almost any price – and these include many of GM's early works. The condition of a book is always a prime factor in its pricing, but the astute collector is well advised to buy a desired book in almost any condition if the price is right, with the mental reservation to replace it later, when possible, with a better copy. In the meantime, that particular text is at hand for comparison and study.

Many people have collected GM's books. One of the most notable runs was in the library of John Quinn, the American lawyer, who had a large library of books and manuscripts of many of the Irish writers, particularly those involved in the 'Celtic Renaissance' at the turn of the century. Since the dispersal of the Quinn collection in 1924, there have been innumerable other sales which have featured long runs of GM's books. A particularly fine collection, now at Cornell University, was formed by Frank Fayant of Fort Plain, New York. He and his wife were friends of GM during the last years of his life, and he reinscribed many of the presentation copies in the Fayant collection, which is also notable for being one of the few of that period to include a considerable number of variants. The collection contains one unique item, *La Ballade de l'Amant Coeur – A Mes Frères d'Armes Burges et Pot*, a poem signed 'Pagan' and later included by GM as 'La Ballade d'Alfred, Alfred aux Belles Dents' in the final revised texts of *Confessions of a Young Man*. Any GM collector should be in seventh heaven to stumble on another copy of this four-page leaflet!

The bibliography of any author who revised and rewrote to the extent that GM did is complicated and presents innumerable problems to the collector as well as to the bibliographer. Is the collection to be comprehensive, as I strongly recommend, and include the many variant texts, or is it to be more restricted, as some will advise, and be confined strictly to first editions? Such a collection in itself will be a major endeavour. Or perhaps the collector may be interested only in final versions of those books which GM placed in the 'canon' of the works by which he wishes to be remembered.

GM briefly explained his criteria for placing books in the authorized canon in the Preface to the final revised 1921 edition of *The Lake*. He also was specific about some of his books which he wished banished into oblivion, although he left two of his most popular books more or less in a state of limbo. He wrote:

I will confess to very little admiration for 'Evelyn Innes' and 'Sister Teresa'. The writing of 'Evelyn Innes' and 'Sister Teresa' was useful to me inasmuch that if I had not written them I could not have written 'The Lake' or 'The Brook Kerith'. It seems ungrateful, therefore, to refuse to allow two of my most successful books into the canon merely because they do not correspond with my aestheticism. But a writer's aestheticism is his all; he cannot surrender it, for his art is dependent upon it, and the single concession he can make is that if an overwhelming demand should arise for these books when he is among the gone – a storm before which the reed must bend – the publisher shall be permitted to print 'Evelyn Innes' and 'Sister Teresa' from the original editions, it being, however, clearly understood that they are offered as apocrypha. But this permission must not be understood to extend to certain books on which my name appears – viz., 'Mike Fletcher', 'Vain Fortune', 'Parnell and His Island'; to some plays, 'Martin Luther', 'The Strike at Arlingford', 'The Bending of the Boughs' [*sic*]; to a couple of volumes of verse entitled 'Pagan Poems' and 'Flowers of Passion' – all of these books, if they are ever reprinted again, should be issued as the work of a disciple – Amico Moorini I put forward as a suggestion.

Of the sixty-six titles listed in the first section ('Books and Pamphlets') of my bibliography, less than forty can be considered major works, and of these GM selected eighteen as his authorized canon. These were published in twenty volumes in the Uniform Edition (Heinemann, London, 1924–1933), but none of the twenty are true first editions and only four of them originally had been published before GM's move to Dublin in 1901. Remainder sheets or the plates of the Uniform Edition were used when, starting in 1936, this edition was reissued as the Ebury Edition. Volumes in this edition have been reprinted many times, and since 1945 it has again been called the Uniform Edition. Just prior to the publication of this canon, GM assented to the publication of the Carra Edition (Boni & Liveright, New York, 1922–1924) in twenty-one volumes, limited to 1,000 sets printed on paper watermarked with GM's signature, and with the first volume signed by GM. This edition includes the two so-called apocryphal books, *Evelyn Innes* and

Sister Teresa printed from the original texts, as well as *Lewis Seymour and Some Women* (the final version of GM's first novel, *A Modern Lover*), *Spring Days*, and *Modern Painting*, all excluded from the Uniform Edition. Two other titles, *Pure Poetry* and *Ulick and Soracha*, were issued in supplementary volumes that matched the format of the Carra Edition but were not actually a part of it. The former was not printed in the Uniform Edition, but the latter was included, not by itself, but in the expanded text of *A Story-Teller's Holiday*. One other volume of the Carra Edition, *In Single Strictness*, was included in the Uniform Edition, but with its title changed to *Celibate Lives* and with the story 'Hugh Monfret' replaced by 'Albert Nobbs' from *A Story-Teller's Holiday*.

It is possible for the collector to still find a complete set of the Carra Edition, and individual volumes are frequently catalogued, as are most of the volumes in the Uniform Edition, which was not issued as a set.

Many of GM's books were issued in luxurious signed limited editions, particularly in his later years, and A. Edward Newton claimed these were 'books obviously written for money'. Harry W. Schwartz, in *This Book Collecting Racket* (Chicago, 1937), while admitting that GM had a better chance of surviving as a collectible author than most of his contemporaries, claimed that he helped perpetuate the limited edition racket by issuing highly priced books, which, he added, were frequently remaindered. Others have described these highly priced books as 'sucker bait' issued only to enrich the author. Facts, however, contradict this calumny, for GM, by his habit of constantly revising to achieve a more perfect style, frequently incurred and paid setting costs that more than offset his profits from a volume. For instance, Francis Meynell of the Nonesuch Press tells in his *My Lives* (London, New York, 1971) of their edition of *Ulick and Soracha*, published in an edition of 1,250 copies at forty-two shillings, a high price in 1926 for a book of 296 pages. He relates that GM

came almost daily . . . to read aloud to us the revisions he had made in his last batch of proofs. Each time it was an entirely new text. The first version was almost illiterate. The second grammatical but undistinguished. The third a transfiguration. It was fascinating to see the process of his composition at close quarters and our feelings were undisturbed by anxieties about the printer's bill, for he had proposed at the outset that he would pay for his own corrections. They exceeded the original cost of printing.

Many of these signed editions, issued on hand-made paper, are first editions of a particular title, although this is not true in all cases. They are important additions to a Moore collection, but so are many of the ephemeral items and the rejected books which GM hoped would be assigned to his disciple, for as Malcolm Brown pointed out in his study, *George Moore: A Reconsideration* (University of Washington Press, 1955), a knowledge of several of these books is necessary to trace accurately his development as a writer.

The most desirable find for a collector would surely be a copy of *Worldliness*, which may or may not have been actually printed, depending on which version of GM's *Confessions of a Young Man* is consulted. In the first text, which GM has described as being 'purely literary', he related the genesis of the play and added, 'Is it necessary to say that I did not find a manager to produce my play? A printer was more attainable and the correction of proofs amused me for a while.' I. A. Williams listed it in his early bibliography (London, New York, etc., 1921) and noted, 'The Author believes, and hopes, that no copy of this, his first published work, now exists'. Just four years previously, however, GM in the fourth revised version of *Confessions* had omitted the reference to *Worldliness* having been been printed and instead said, 'I learnt . . . that it would be well to have my play copied and the stage directions inscribed in red ink'.

GM's contradictory memories of *Worldliness* (added to the fact that no contemporary mention of it has been found, including none in the author's own correspondence, and that there is no record of anyone ever having seen a copy) lead me to believe that the play, as a printed book, never existed. The GM collector should keep the title in the back of his mind, however, with the pleasant hope that he could be the one who some day might discover a copy hidden amid other dusty books in a bookseller's bin. In his search, he might also recall that Williams lists it as having been issued in 'pink wrappers'.

Flowers of Passion, described a number of times by GM as being his 'first book', and *Pagan Poems* are two of the earliest titles he rejected; both should be of the greatest interest to the collector and student of GM's writings, for not only do they contain the germs of several of his later works but a number of the poems in the second volume were revised for inclusion in later works. Revision was not a habit developed in GM's old age, as has been stated by a number of critics, but a life-long preoccupation with achieving perfection. It was first manifested in *Pagan Poems* in which five of the poems were revised and reprinted from his previous book of verse.

There are two states of *Flowers of Passion*, one having plain edges and the other gilt, with no priority of issue established. Very likely the two states were issued simultaneously at different prices, as was the custom at that period, but some collectors seem to prefer a copy with the gilt edges, possibly because of its more luxurious appearance. On the other hand, the presumably early copy in the Fayant collection given by GM to his mother has plain edges. *Pagan Poems* is found in three forms, the first being the one most generally favoured by collectors, though the actual text of all three is identical, and any one of the three should be a welcome addition to any GM collection. It appears that shortly after the book was published and an undetermined number of copies had been issued, a dispute arose between author and publisher and the title-page was removed from the remaining copies. It never has been clearly established who was responsible for the mutilation. Some say the page was torn out by the publisher, while others claim it was done by GM. Regardless of who it was, the act was the first step in creating two additional states of the book. Those copies that were originally issued include the title-page as an integral part of the first gathering and have GM's autograph initials written in ink across the lower right hand corner of the publisher's imprint on the title-page. It has been frequently stated, based on a 1930 inscription by GM in one of the copies with an original title-page, that only twenty copies of this form exist, but this is a mistake, for there are more than twenty presentation copies now in various public and private collections, and in addition several more extant copies are uninscribed except for the initials on the title-page. (The copy in my former collection is one of these.) There appears to be a fairly large number of copies without the title-page, and also there is a sizable number of copies which have been sophisticated by the insertion of a new title-leaf tipped on the stub of the original leaf. The paper and type used for this duplicate page are slightly different from the original.

The third of the early trio of rejected books is the play *Martin Luther*, another novice attempt by GM to master the art of playwriting (something he never really accomplished, but it was an art form which he pursued all his life). The play was written with Bernard Lopez, a professional French hack, if we can judge by the nearly two dozen names listed on the title page as those with whom he had served as a 'collaborateur'. All known copies of the play seem identical, allowing for the ravages of sun and time, except for the one described by another early GM bibliographer, Henry Danielson, whose work was published as an appendix to John Freeman's *A Portrait of George Moore in a Study of His Work* (London, New York, 1922). The apparently unique copy that he describes is bound in red rather than the usual bluish-grey cloth and has Lopez's first name spelled 'Bernardo' on the spine. This copy, he says, has a binder's label pasted on the rear end-paper, so it may have been a special binding, done for some now unrecorded occasion. Another impression of *Martin Luther*, in wrappers rather than cloth binding, was issued apparently to send to theatrical managers in the hope of securing the play's production. This impression was printed from the same setting of type as the regular edition but on a slightly larger page, with the introductory poems and Preface omitted, and page numbers and signature letters altered. Each of the printings is scarce, but the one in wrappers seems to be the more difficult to find.

Les Cloches de Corneville Lyrics by George and Augustus Moore printed circa 1883 'for private circulation' is known to me in a single copy formerly in the library of George Sims, unrecorded until it was sold in 1923 at Hodgson's auction rooms in London. By an act of serendipity, I chanced upon this copy more than thirty years ago, along with another rarity, *Walnuts and Wine: A Christmas Annual* edited by Augustus Moore, which contains an early and never reprinted GM story. Needless to say, I purchased both. It has been said that another copy of the *Lyrics* exists, but this has not been verified.

These lyrics were used in a production of the operetta that opened in London on 29 March 1883, for a run of ten days, an event that marked the first time GM's name appeared on a playbill. It is possible that the lyrics were also used for the touring company which GM joined at Henley as an observer to obtain background material for *A Mummer's Wife*. The collector aspiring to locate a copy of this rare pamphlet should be aware that several times a complete translation of the Offenbach opera comique has been catalogued as being the one by the brothers Moore. Actually, this is the standard translation by H.B. Farnie and R. Reece in the first printing of the J. Williams edition, although it does not list their names on the title page as later impressions do. Some of the lyrics in the Moore translation were used, slightly revised, by GM in chapters XV and XVI of *A Mummer's Wife*, and a comparison of these with the same lyrics in the Farnie and Reece version show that they are quite different. It has also been stated by an expert on the 1890s in London (who received his information, he told me, from a provincial bookseller) that Farnie and Reece were the pen-names of Augustus and George Moore. This is clearly an error, for Farnie and Reece were well known writers and adaptors of French operettas for the English stage in the 1880s.

These early works are of interest to the student and collector for the part they played in GM's development, as is his first published novel, *A Modern Lover*, issued in 1883 in three volumes. There are two distinct binding states, differentiated by the angle of the date on the front cover, plus at least two 'trial' bindings. Sets are scarce because a large portion of the printing was destroyed in a warehouse fire. The collector would be well advised to purchase any set offered, as it is the only edition which has GM's original text. The next edition, published in one volume, presents a revised and expanded text. This edition was reprinted a number of times by Vizetelly, GM's new publisher, and in the United States by several different publishers, so copies of this expanded text, if not always the first printing, are to be found from time to time. Nearly thirty-five years after its first publication GM again rewrote the story as *Lewis Seymour and Some Women*, discussed below.

GM's next book was *A Mummer's Wife*, the earliest of his works to be included in his canon. Its publication by Vizetelly as a one-volume novel in November 1884 (dated 1885 on the title-page) was a significant step in ending the virtual monopoly of the circulating libraries that had dominated British publishing for many years by guaranteeing the sale of a substantial number of any 'approved' triple-decker priced at thirty-one shillings sixpence, a price that made them prohibitive for the average buyer. Thus, GM's book, the first by a major writer issued in a single volume at six shillings, has a premier place in British publishing history. There were a number of impressions, designated on the title page as variously numbered editions, of which copies are available from time to time. A year after first publication a new edition was published, slightly revised and with an author's Preface added. This was reprinted several times, and it was also published in the United States, in an unauthorized edition, as *An Actor's Wife*. Later Brentano's issued an authorized edition under its original title. The final printing of this text was in 1917 in the Brentano Uniform Edition. It was almost immediately superseded in the series by a completely revised text. This was the first edition of GM's final version, the one used for all subsequent printings, including the two collected editions. Although not the first volume issued, it is volume one in the Uniform Edition, where it is preceded by GM's final work, *A Communication to My Friends*, uncompleted at the time of his death and written to be a preface to his collected works.

GM's next published work was one of the major shells fired in the battle against the circulating libraries, which steadfastly refused to stock his books because they feared some of their provincial customers might object to his alleged outspokenness. It was

Literature at Nurse or Circulating Morals, a three-penny pamphlet published by Vizetelly in 1885. Copies are scarce and generally fairly high in price when offered, but for the collector who wants only the text, there is a modern reprint (Hassocks, 1976) that also includes GM's earlier article, 'A New Censorship of Literature', from the *Pall Mall Gazette*, plus the ensuing correspondence in that paper.

GM's next three novels, *A Drama in Muslin*, *A Mere Accident* and *Spring Days*, present no real problems to the collector. All were published by Vizetelly in the 'one-volume novels' series, and subsequent impressions are called 'editions' on the title-pages. The first was later reissued by Walter Scott; there was no American edition. Brentano's was listed as co-publisher on the title-page for the second, and the third was published in the United States, in an unauthorized edition, as *Shifting Love*.

In *A Drama in Muslin*, GM turned to his native Ireland for inspiration and setting, and although he revised and republished the story in 1915 as *Muslin*, most commentators prefer the earlier text. Richard Allen Cave in his *A Study of the Novels of George Moore* (Gerrards Cross, 1978) says, 'In revising the novel . . . Moore attempted to overcome . . . [the] problem of style by heavily cutting all the lyrical passages, but the loss was greater than the gain'. A. Norman Jeffares, in the introduction to a recent reprint of the original text (Gerrards Cross, 1981), concludes '*A Drama in Muslin* remains with its mixture of satire and sympathy, objectivity and panoramic range of vision one of its creator's most intelligent insights into human life'. *A Mere Accident* has never been republished as such, and although GM was displeased with it, he continued working on it and rewrote it as 'John Norton', one of the three stories included nine years later in *Celibates*. In spite of the fact that GM lost faith in *Spring Days*, he later revised it and reissued it in 1912 with a new Preface under its original title. This text was included in the Carra Edition, but it found no place in the Uniform Edition.

Ireland was again the setting of *Parnell and His Island*, a caustic survey of Moore's native land and its people, described by Malcolm Brown as 'a hysterical anti-Irish pamphlet published at the height of the Home Rule agitation'. It was to haunt him a decade later when he embraced and became a part of the Irish literary resurgence. It is a collection of articles originally written for translation into French for the weekly *Le Figaro*, where they were presented as 'Lettres sur l'Irlande' in six issues during the summer of 1886, then gathered together and published early in 1887 as *Terre d'Irlande*. Three sections were added by GM to the original group for the book in English issued three months later in both cloth and paper wrappers. The two forms were reissued in 1891, possibly to take advantage of the publicity surrounding Parnell's death.

One of GM's most enduring books, and one which he kept revising for thirty years, is *Confessions of a Young Man*, first serialized in 1887 and then published the next year. Its printing history is an involved one, but suffice to say that in addition to its serial version and translation into French for both serial and book publication, there are four separate English texts. The various editions are detailed in my bibliography, and most are available from time to time in the market place. For a concise text with the major additions and deletions indicated, plus reasonably complete variorum notes and the text of the several Prefaces, the textual collector and scholar is referred to the edition edited by Susan Dick (McGill-Queen's University Press, Montreal and London, 1972). This contains the text of the original edition plus the changes made in the 1889, 1904, and 1916 revisions. The book is the first by GM cast in an autobiographical mould, where, after the first edition, the narrator becomes 'George Moore'. In most of his fiction, however, from *A Modern Lover* through the first edition of *The Untilled Field*, there is a character called Harding, an author, who seems to be speaking for GM and is an extension of his personality.

Mike Fletcher was the book GM abjured with the greatest vehemence. Its publishing history is relatively simple, as there were only two editions, one published in London in 1889, the other in New York in 1890 (dated 1889 on the title-page). Remainder sheets of the London edition were reissued in a different binding with the date on the title-page omitted but with '1899' stamped at the foot of the spine. It seems possible that these may have been issued for colonial distribution as the few copies seen all appear to have originated in Canada.

In addition to being a novelist, GM also was an active journalist, contributing articles on literature, art, and other topics to a number of leading periodicals, including *The Speaker*, where he served for more than four years as its art critic. Two volumes of his critical writings were published after the fiasco of *Mike Fletcher*, which was either ignored or harshly treated by the critics. These two books, *Impressions and Opinions* in 1891 and *Modern Painting* in 1893, helped redeem his sagging reputation. First-edition copies of both are frequently found, though a collector seeking them is again referred to my bibliography for specific details of the various states of the first editions. Both had American impressions, stereotype plates being used for the first, and sheets of the English edition for the second. *Impressions and Opinions* was reissued in a revised edition in 1913 with two new articles replacing two omitted ones. An expanded edition of *Modern Painting* was published in 1896, and there was also an American impression, both of which were reprinted a number of times. GM permitted the book to be included in the Carra Edition, with the text further expanded by the inclusion of 'Degas' from *Impressions and Opinions*. Other articles from the book served as the basis of portions of *Conversations in Ebury Street*.

The textual history of *Vain Fortune*, another of the books which GM suggested should be attributed to Amico Moorini, is complicated. It was originally serialized in *Lady's Pictorial* whose 'chaste' readers were unaware that the story was by that 'wicked' George Moore, for his identity was hidden under a *nom de plume*, 'Lady Rhone'. The cat, however, was shortly out of the bag, for *Vain Fortune* was soon published with GM's name listed as author. There was also a limited edition of 150 copies signed by the publisher rather than the author. This was the first of GM's books to be issued in a special luxurious format. Neither edition apparently was successful, for both were later reissued in different bindings by another publisher. There was also an unauthorized paperbound American edition, published about two months before an authorized revised edition appeared in New York but not in London. GM was dissatisfied with the original text, and in preparing the revised edition, he altered the sequence of events. This version also displeased him, though in 1922 in a conversation with Barret H. Clark (*Intimate Portraits*, New York, 1951), he indicated that it was this edition he would like to use as the basis for a further reworking of the story, and at one point he contemplated changing the title to *An Autumn Tragedy*. After the 1892 version was published, GM continued revising, adding 'only flesh and muscle . . . and I think a little life', as he explained in a 'Prefatory Note' to the 1895 edition published only in England. It was never actually further revised or reprinted.

Many have written of the challenge of George Sims to the Independent Theatre, in which GM was actively engaged, that it produce an original realistic play by an English dramatist. Sims offered £100 to finance its presentation. GM's play, *The Strike at Arlingford*, was the response, and shortly after it was produced in 1893, it was published in book form. Its sale was limited, but copies of both the first edition and the American issue are frequently seen.

In the early part of October 1893, 'Pages from the Life of a

Workgirl' by GM was serialized in the London daily *Pall Mall Gazette*. This was the first appearance of a portion of the story published the following March as *Esther Waters*. It met with both critical and popular success and is still considered by many as being GM's finest achievement. The first impression has a plain front cover; the lettering and floral design on most copies were added on the binding of later impressions. It is certainly the most reprinted of any of GM's works, but because of certain incidents in the story, considered 'daring' for the 1890s, the book was not accepted for publication by an American publisher. As a consequence, there was no authorized 'copyright' edition in the United States. But where more respectable publishers feared to tread, the pirates did not, and upon news of the book's successful debut in England there were soon nearly two dozen editions for American readers to choose from. Copies of these, many in somewhat lurid paper covers, are still found from time to time in dealers' bins. The first edition text was used for continental circulation, and this text has also been used for at least two modern reprints with critical introductions by Professors Malcolm Brown (New York, 1958), and Helmut E. Gerber (Chicago, 1977).

As usual, publication was no sooner achieved than GM started his process of revision, tightening the text by the omission of some passages, and with a few small additions trying 'to finish what I left unfinished', as he explained in a Preface added to the paperbound, sixpenny edition in which the new text appeared. This revised version was also used for an authorized copyright edition in the United States, and the plates of this edition were later used by two other publishers. It was also this 1899 revised text that was used as the basic text of the edition of *Esther Waters* edited by Professor Lionel Stevenson (Boston, 1963), whose analysis of the text and the inclusion of two appendices detailing the textual differences between the 1894 and 1899 editions and those between the 1899 and 1920 editions makes this an extremely valuable book for the GM scholar. The process of revision continued, and a final version was published in 1920 in a regular edition and shortly afterwards in a signed, limited edition that matched the first editions of several other GM books first published around this time (individually noted below). There were a few minor revisions in the 1926 impression, and this was the text used for many of the subsequent reprints, some of which are still in print. GM also saw dramatic possibilities in the story, and a play based on a portion of it was produced for two performances in December 1911 by the Stage Society. The text of this version, *Esther Waters: A Play*, was published in January 1913, with an American impression published three months later in Boston.

In addition to the previously noted 'John Norton', the rewritten version of *A Mere Accident*, GM's next book, *Celibates*, contains two other stories, 'Mildred Lawson', expanded and rewritten from its periodical appearance as 'An Art Student', and 'Agnes Lahens', previously unpublished. Sheets of the first edition were used for a colonial issue, and there were separate American and continental editions. The plates of the former were used when the title was included twenty years later in the Brentano Uniform Edition. Of the three stories, the theme of the first was reworked for 'Hugh Monfret', published in *In Single Strictness*; the second was rewritten as 'Henrietta Marr' for inclusion in the same book and later in *Celibate Lives*.

GM's next major effort was the novel *Evelyn Innes*, which expanded as he worked upon it to such an extent that he had to divide the story into two parts, with the second, called *Sister Teresa*, published three years after the first portion appeared. The two books were among his most successful, as far as public response went, but because of his revisions and his reworking of the story for nearly every new printing and edition, their publishing history is tangled. The first edition of *Evelyn Innes*, published 8 June 1898, had barely appeared when GM started revising and adding new material, and a second edition, identical in format and with no indication that it was anything but a new impression, was published in August. Sheets remaining from the first printing were used for a colonial edition. Still dissatisfied, GM continued tinkering with the text through a trial revised edition of twelve specially prepared copies, a continental edition, and two paperbound ones, for a total of five distinct texts. (Once again I refer the collector to my bibliography for details regarding the alterations in these various versions.) Then there was also a different text for the American edition, which GM disowned due to expurgations and changes made by the publisher. The story is much the same for *Sister Teresa*, first published 8 July 1901, revised only twice. There were American and colonial editions using the original text; a trial revised edition of twenty copies, with this text being used for the continental edition; and the final revision published eight years after the first edition. Twenty years later this final text was used in a reprint series, with *Evelyn Innes* printed as a companion volume, but with its first text used, resulting in a disconnected narrative. Earlier, when GM relented and permitted the two to be printed in the Carra Edition, he insisted that first-edition texts be used.

During the period GM was writing the divided novel, his assistance was sought by W.B. Yeats and Edward Martyn for the Irish Literary Theatre, about to make its debut in Dublin. GM agreed, and as a result became involved in the writing of two of the plays produced. Martyn's *Tale of a Town* was rewritten as *The Bending of the Bough*, to which Martyn refused to let his name be attached, so GM's name was listed as sole author when the play was presented on 20 April 1901, and on the text of the play which was published the following day in London. Then, within a few days, at GM's insistence, a revised text was issued. The collector can distinguish the first edition by the fact that it has 156 pages of text and that there is a double ornament following the author's name on the title-page. The ornaments are omitted from the second edition, which has but 145 pages of text. An American edition was published after the second English one, but its text is in an intermediate state between the other two. More recently there has been another American edition, edited by Professor William J. Feeney (Chicago, 1969), which combines the text of the American and second English editions. In this, GM's Preface, printed in the other three editions, is omitted, but the editor provides an Introduction that relates the tale of the play's genesis and its background in Irish politics.

The other play that GM was involved in at this time was *Diarmuid and Grania*, written with Yeats as co-author. Diverse accounts of its writing have been given by many, including each of its authors. It was not published during the lifetime of either of them and did not see print until 1951, when it was published first in a periodical, then as an offprint of only twenty-five copies. Later it was included in *The Variorum Edition of the Plays of W.B. Yeats* (London, and New York, 1966) and was printed separately in an edition with an introduction by Anthony Farrow (Chicago, 1974).

In 1901 GM shifted his residence from London to Dublin. In addition to his theatrical activities there he wrote a series of stories to be translated into Irish to be used in the revival of that language. Some of these stories were published in magazines, and a number were gathered together and published as a book in Irish – 'in the hope of furnishing the young Irish of the future with models', explained GM in the Preface of the 1914 English edition. English versions of some of the stories also appeared in periodicals, and these and others were published as *The Untilled Field* in London on 30 April 1903 and a couple of months later in the United States. A continental edition was published the same year, with two stories omitted and others revised. The rewriting continued with a second revision in 1914, a third in 1928, and a final one in 1931, which included a new story based on the subject matter of the two omitted from all editions after the first. The latest edition (Gerrards Cross, 1976) reprints the final text and also includes the two omitted stories as an appendix.

One of the stories originally intended for inclusion in *The Untilled Field*, but which grew too large as GM developed it, was *The Lake*. It was published separately on 10 November 1905, and again GM immediately started revising. Near the end of the month a second edition, listed as a 'second impression', was published, with minor revisions throughout and with the central portion of the book completely rewritten. Remainder sheets of the first printing, and later those of the second printing, were used when the title was included in Heinemann's Colonial Library. The publication of a continental edition followed, but with an intermediate text. The American edition has the same text as the first edition. A final revision was published in 1921, with the names of two of the leading characters changed and with a new Preface, portions of which I quoted earlier. A recent edition, with a splendid Afterword by Richard Allen Cave (Gerrards Cross, 1980), reprints not only the final text, but also two omitted chapters, one from the first version and the other from the second.

Memoirs of My Dead Life, GM's next major publication, followed in June 1906. The sketches or stories in it are reprinted for the most part from various periodicals where the originals appeared during the previous decade. The American edition is notable for GM's preface, 'Apologia pro Scriptis Meis', appearing in no other edition, which wryly comments on expurgations made by the publishers in two of the stories. Further impressions in August 1906 and March 1908 of the first edition have minor revisions. The continental edition follows the text of the second impression, except for the omission of two stories and the addition of about twenty pages of new material. A new story was added to the 1915 edition, and limited editions published in the United States in 1920 and in England in 1921 each show further additions and revisions. A final text, showing more revisions and deletions, was published in 1928 in the Uniform Edition.

In 1911 GM left Dublin to return to London, where he lived for the rest of his life. Prior to his departure he had completed the first volume of the autobiographical *Hail and Farewell!*, in which he attempted 'to take a certain amount of material and to model it just as he would do in a novel'. His subject was not only himself but the real people connected with the Irish literary renaissance, told sometimes in hilarious detail, sparing none, including an often rather ludicrous GM, in the recital of the frequently preposterous events. The book was published in three volumes, *Ave* in October 1911, *Salve* in October 1912, and *Vale* in March 1914. American and continental editions also were published, with the latter containing some additional material in the third segment. Later impressions of the English edition of *Vale* have a brief passage deleted, and still later ones include the material added to the continental edition. A two-volume revised edition with a new preface, 'Art Without the Artist', was published in 1925 in a signed, limited edition and in the United States in a regular trade edition. The final text was included in three volumes in the Uniform Edition. An annotated edition in one volume (Gerrards Cross, 1976), edited by Dr. Cave, prints the final text and also includes as appendices the original chapter VI of *Vale* and other material having a bearing on the story.

The Brook Kerith, described by one GM scholar (Professor Walter James Miller) as being 'one of the major novels of the twentieth century', had long occupied GM's thoughts. He traced its origins to the gift of a Bible from a dear friend at the turn of the century. His first working of the subject was in the scenario for a play, *The Apostle*, first printed in a periodical and then in book form in 1911. This book, published in both Dublin and Boston, has 'A Prefatory Letter on Reading the Bible for the First Time', previously published in both English and German reviews but found nowhere else, making this title a desirable addition to any GM collection. The theme continued to fascinate GM, and in the spring of 1914 he visited the Holy Land to gather atmosphere for the book, finally published on 23 August 1916, in both London and New York. There was also an edition deluxe of 250 numbered and signed copies. In almost every succeeding impression there were revisions until a final text was achieved in the 1927 version published in the Uniform Edition. This text was also used for signed, limited editions, illustrated with twelve engravings by Stephen Gooden, published in both London and New York.

A dramatization of a portion of *The Brook Kerith* was published in a limited, signed edition in 1923, which was again called *The Apostle*. GM continued working on the dramatisation, and it was produced as *The Passing of the Essenes* for six performances in 1930 at London's Arts Theatre. This was published in both England and the United States in limited editions. A revised version with a Preface was included in 1931 as a volume in the Uniform Edition.

Two of GM's earlier books were republished about this time in rewritten versions with new titles. *Muslin (A Drama in Muslin)* was published in 1915 with a Preface by the author, explaining his revisions, and *Lewis Seymour and Some Women (A Modern Lover)*, also with a new Preface, appeared in 1917. Both were published in the United States, the latter preceding the English edition, as volumes in the Brentano Uniform Edition; both were included in the Carra Edition. The second was volume one in that set and was prefaced by another 'Apologia Pro Scriptis Meis' as the general introduction to the Carra Edition. It was not included in the Uniform Edition, although *Muslin* was.

It has been said that every author should have at least one 'joyous book', and GM's was *A Story-Teller's Holiday*, a sort of Irish *Droll Stories*, wherein are told many of the country's lusty folk tales. Fearing censorship, a fictitious Society of Irish Folklore was invoked as publisher, and the first signed, limited edition was issued in July 1918 by Cumann Sean-eolais na h-Eireann in London. An American limited edition was issued in September. The book was included in the Carra Edition. An expanded and revised edition in two volumes was published in the United States in 1928 in a signed, limited edition, printed on the same watermarked paper used for the Carra Edition. In addition to being revised throughout, two stories, one previously published in a magazine, plus *Ulick and Soracha*, were added. The latter was published separately in 1926 in limited editions in both England and the United States. This new text was included in two volumes in the Uniform Edition.

During his years in Ireland and after his return to England GM continued contributing articles to various periodicals, and some of these served as the basis for sections of two books in which he revived the conversational structure for forays into literary and art criticism. These 'imaginary conversations', with many of his friends as interlocutors, were first gathered together in *Avowals*, issued in a signed, limited edition in 1919 by the fictitious Society of Irish Folklore, though certainly none of the material in the book could be considered lurid enough to prohibit regular publication. There was also an American limited edition, which was reprinted, with the omission of one section, in the Carra Edition and later in a trade edition. GM revised the text of *Avowals* for its inclusion in the Uniform Edition. Five years later another group of similar critical articles was published in 1924 as *Conversations in Ebury Street* in a signed, limited edition. The same year it was included in the Carra Edition with the addition of the section transferred from *Avowals*. This was reprinted in a trade edition. A new section was added when *Conversations in Ebury Street* was included in the Uniform Edition, and this text was used when it was added to the Landmark Library in 1969.

GM's preoccupation with the theatre started early in his career and continued throughout his creative life. This has been touched upon in the discussion of *Worldliness*, *Martin Luther*, *Les Cloches de Corneville*, *Esther Waters*: *A Play* and the plays he helped write for the Irish Literary Theatre, but there are a number of others, some of which were published separately and should be of interest to the collector.

GM collaborated with many in pursuing his ambition to be a successful dramatist. One of these was Mrs. Pearl Craigie, a popular novelist of the 1890s and early 1900s who signed her books 'John Oliver Hobbes'. One of their plays, *Journeys End in Lovers Meeting*, was used in 1894–95 by Ellen Terry as a curtain-raiser, with GM's name listed as co-author on the playbill and in the reviews, but when it was published in 1902 by Mrs. Craigie, she failed to mention GM's part in its writing. Act One of another joint effort, *The Fool's Hour*, was published in the first volume of *The Yellow Book*, April 1894, with both of their names listed as authors. Later they also worked on another play, variously called *The Three Lovers* and *The Peacock's Feathers*, which GM continued revising after Mrs. Craigie's death. The play, now called *Elizabeth Cooper*, was produced in London by the Stage Society on 23 June 1913, and the next month it was published in Dublin and Boston. GM's friend, Edouard Dujardin, helped with the script, and a French translation by him was produced in Paris as *Clara Florise* in 1914. This version was later published in a French periodical. Revising continued on the script, now called *The Coming of Gabrielle*, in hope of a production, but when Nigel Playfair put it in rehearsal, GM balked at the demanded cuts and was generally dissatisfied with what was being done to the play, so he withdrew it. The script was published in 1920 in a limited, signed edition in London, and the following year in New York. Other revisions continued. In 1922 a revised continental edition was published, and with still more revision it was finally performed in London for three performances in July 1923.

Another script upon which GM worked for many years was about the possibility that others had written Shakespeare's plays. This was *The Making of an Immortal*, and it was published in New York and London on 8 December 1927, in a limited, signed edition. The playlet was produced in London by an all-star cast in a gala performance on 1 April 1928, and it may be that some see the date as being significant, considering the play's theme.

GM's last major novel, *Héloïse and Abélard*, was privately printed in a two-volume signed, limited edition issued in London on 17 February 1921. As was expected, GM immediately saw flaws in it, and he produced a pamphlet, *Fragments from Héloïse & Abélard*, with alternative material to replace a passage in the second volume, plus some other corrections and additions. This material was sent to his New York publisher, who did not include the additions and corrections in their proper places, but instead printed them in an eight-page gathering inserted between pages 18 and 19. The text of this edition, with additions and corrections in their proper places, was issued in the Carra Edition. Trade editions followed, first in two volumes and then in one. In 1925 *Héloïse and Abélard* was added to the Uniform Edition in a single volume.

In Single Strictness, mentioned before as containing revised versions of two stories from *Celibates*, was published in limited, signed editions in July 1922 in London and two months later in New York. GM was still not pleased with 'Hugh Monfret', the story using the same theme as 'John Norton', and so when it came to including it in the Carra Edition a new and shorter ending was supplied for the story. At the same time the new ending was printed on six pages, and these GM sent to friends to insert in their presentation copies. Even with its new ending, 'Hugh Monfret' failed to please GM, and when *In Single Strictness* was reissued in 1927 as *Celibate Lives*, the story was replaced by 'Albert Nobbs', transferred from *A Story-Teller's Holiday*. *Celibate Lives* was printed in London in the Uniform Edition; in New York in a trade edition, matching several other GM titles; and in a continental edition. Its most recent printing was in the Landmark Library (London, 1968).

Three other titles, all first published in 1924, should be noted. They are *Pure Poetry*, an anthology edited by GM; *The Pastoral Loves of Daphnis and Chloe* done into English by GM; and *Peronnik the Fool*, an old Breton legend, supposedly written by Héloïse, according to GM 'so that she might teach her son French (he had been away in Brittany for a long time and came back to her speaking Breton)'. GM's definition of 'pure poetry' is 'something that the poet creates outside of his own personality' and described by another as being 'lasting objects of verbal beauty and imagination that serve no purpose other than poetic enjoyment'. GM's selection of such poems is still the only one attempted. The anthology was first printed in a limited, numbered edition by the Nonesuch Press, and it has never been reprinted in Great Britain. It was also printed in the United States in a limited, numbered edition, issued as a supplementary volume to the Carra

Edition. This was reprinted the next year in a trade edition, and nearly fifty years later a paper-bound edition was published. GM's translation of *Daphnis and Chloë*, based on the French translation by Jacques Amyot of the Longus story, was published in a signed, limited edition in London and with *Peronnik the Fool* as the final volume of the Carra Edition. It has been reprinted in England a number of times, including in the Uniform Edition, and in a Folio Society volume illustrated by Marcel Vertes. In the United States it was reprinted by the Limited Editions Club, illustrated with engravings by Ruth Reeves. Interestingly enough, this is the only edition to indicate on the title page that Longus was the author of the original story. The type of this edition was reproduced enlarged for the text of an edition published in New York, featuring forty illustrations by Marc Chagall. The publication of *Peronnik* is interesting as its first edition was the Carra Edition printing with *Daphnis and Chloe*, previously noted, and its first separate printing was also in the United States, in a limited edition designed by Bruce Rogers and published by William Edwin Rudge. A revised edition next appeared in France: it was the first book published by Nancy Cunard at her Hours Press. The first English edition did not appear until after GM's death, when it was issued, again in the same volume as *Daphnis and Chloë*, in the Uniform Edition. Later in the year a signed, limited edition was published in London with engravings by Stephen Gooden. GM had signed the pages containing the limitation notice prior to his death.

GM's last novel, *Aphrodite in Aulis*, was published in 1930 in a sumptuous limited, signed edition that was issued in both Great Britain and the United States. This book was no exception to GM's revising habits, and within a few months a revised edition was published first in the United States and then in the Uniform Edition. In his final days GM was actively working on another novel, *Madeline de Lisle*, which was never completed nor published, and on a survey of his complete literary life. Only partially revised when he died, the latter was published posthumously by the Nonesuch Press in a limited edition as *A Communication to My Friends* and then added as a preface to the Uniform Edition in the same volume as *A Mummer's Wife*, the earliest book GM had admitted to his canon.

A number of other books will be of interest to the GM collector: several volumes of letters, with more promised in the near future; a number of ephemeral publications in addition to those previously mentioned, such as *The Royal Academy 1895*, a pamphlet with 'Criticisms' by GM and 'Caricatures' by Harry Furniss;

Reminiscences of the Impressionist Painters issued in Dublin as one of the Tower Press Booklets and later incorporated in *Vale*; GM's brief reverie, *The Talking Pine*, the last publication of the Hours Press; the short story, *A Flood*, issued in an edition of 185 copies; plus several occasional publications and books with prefaces and other contributions by GM. Also there are translations of some of GM's books and stories into at least a dozen different languages, any one of which would be a welcome addition to an avid GM Collector.

As I intimated at the outset of this survey on collecting GM's works, the search may be a long one, particularly if a collection of the many variant texts is to be assembled. Such a challenge certainly should not discourage a collector worthy of the name. My advice is to have the same persistence in collecting that GM had in revising and rewriting, always striving for a completeness as he strove for perfection. For me, forming a GM collection was a long and happy avocation.

Appendix

SOME BIBLIOGRAPHICAL NOTES

EDWIN GILCHER

When *A Bibliography of George Moore* (Northern Illinois University Press, 1970) was published, it was expected that there would be omissions and that more material, as well as greater detail about some entries, would come to light as research continued. This has proven to be true, particularly in the 'Periodical Appearances' section, and these additions and others, plus some corrections of typographical errors, will be included in a *Supplement* to the bibliography now being compiled. Not all of the new material, particularly notes regarding subsequent impressions of the various editions and similar information, will be included and this must await an expanded and corrected edition of the bibliography some time in the future.

It is the purpose of these notes to share with others interested in Moore and his works some of the new information prior to the publication of the *Supplement*. An egregious misprint, a misspelling of a misspelling, in footnote 2 on page 32 should perhaps be mentioned first. The footnote deals with an 'advance' or 'pre-publication' state of *Impressions and Opinions* (A15–a), where the misprint on the title-page of 'A Humorous Wife' for 'A Mummer's Wife' was escalated by a misprint in the bibliography to 'A Hummerous Wife' which escaped detection while the book was in proof. The error was first brought to public attention by Josiah O. Bennett, cataloguer for the Lilly Library of Indiana University, in a bibliographical note, 'More on Moore', in *The Serif*, the quarterly of the Kent State University libraries, March 1971. His notes also listed a number of minor differences between the 'advance' and regular copies of the first edition.

There also were a number of perplexing problems which seem to have been solved. Among these is the 'preliminary state' of the first edition of *Confessions of a Young Man* (A12–a) mentioned in footnote 2 of that entry. It had 'an unflattering photographic frontispiece of the author' rather than the etched portrait by William Strang found in the regular edition. The information about this came from a note in *The Papers of the Bibliographical Society of America*, Volume 36, First Quarter 1942, by Howard Mott, who had purchased this copy at the dispersal of the Frank Deardon library. When asked about the location of the copy he replied that he did not then know its whereabouts, but shortly after the publication of the bibliography he informed me that he had finally discovered that it is in the Morgan Library in New York, where I was soon after permitted to examine it.

This copy, which may be unique, differs in several particulars from the regular edition, in addition to the frontispiece. It is bound in red buckram over bevelled boards and is stamped in gilt with fancy initial letters on the spine and front cover. Mr. Mott had stated in his PBSA note that 'it is said that Moore objected to this (understandably) and the etched frontispiece of William Strang was substituted after about twenty copies with the earlier frontispiece had been released.' The use of this photographic frontispiece had originally been suggested by GM, who in a letter to Herbert Wigram, an editor of the publishers, wrote, 'I think it would be well to print my portrait in the confessions. It would attract attention for I have a photograph that is very like the author of the confession.' Seemingly the way it was reproduced was what displeased GM, for the etched portrait which replaced it was based on the photograph.

Apparently no copies of the book were actually distributed, but Wigram wrote GM 8 December 1887, 'We have sent advance sheets (with portrait) to America,' so it seems probable that the binding on the Morgan copy was done in the United States. No other copies with the photographic frontispiece have been located, but it is possible that other bound or unbound sets of the sheets are extant. This seems likely as an article about GM, 'A Rising Novelist' (by Clara Lanza, in the *New York World*, 21 April 1889) was illustrated with a picture similar to the photograph used in these early sheets and the same picture also was used with a review of *Celibates* by Harry Thurston Peck in *The Bookman* (New York), June 1885.

An old saying has it that 'No book is completed until *Error* has crept in & affixed his sly Imprimatur.' This dubious 'erronical' blessing was bestowed on the bibliography, and evidence of it is not more apparent than in the section devoted to the entries for *Evelyn Innes* (A22). The most noticeable, perhaps, is the mixed numbering of the various editions, with two different ones being numbered the same. The Tauchnitz continental and Appleton American editions, through some inexplicable mischance, share the same sub-number 2a. The former, in addition, is misdated – it was actually published in 1898. When the misnumbering error was discovered it was seen that the Appleton edition should have been listed as 5a and its sub-edition, the Appleton Dollar Library, should have been 5a2.

These tentative renumberings are no longer valid, for there is now evidence from GM's correspondence that the first English edition (a) was published 8 June, rather than in May, the date assigned to it by the weight of evidence at the time the bibliography was published. The date now known to be correct makes it follow the Appleton edition, published 2 June, thus making the latter the true first edition.

In order not to disturb too drastically the rest of the numbering in this section, the American edition is being moved ahead of the English edition with a new entry designation of aa being assigned to it, and aa2 will indicate the sub-edition.

Perhaps it is fitting that the Appleton edition should be in such an ambiguous position, for GM practically repudiated it and wrote to a friend that it was 'shamefully expurgated for the American market.' There are 'fifty-eight major changes' in the text according to Dr. John Denny Fischer who carefully compared the various versions for his unpublished variorum edition. It is possible that a few of these may have been last minute changes made by GM on the proofs of the English edition, but most were deletions of material deemed 'unsuitable' for American readers. The bowdlerization of the book, however, was done with GM's consent for Appleton's by George William Sheldon. In a letter to him, dated 5 April 1898, GM wrote, '. . . I should prefer not to discuss the alterations which you intend to make in the text of my novel. I am quite settled about the text I shall publish in England but as has always been understood you are free to edit the book as you see fit for America.' Later, in a letter to Unwin, dated 4 May 1898, GM wrote, 'I have just looked through the proof amended by Shelton [*sic*], some of his suppressions are beyond me . . . But as I have said the American version does not concern me.'

Another error in this section, this an omission, is a dropped line in the collation of the fourth edition (e) and there should be inserted between the third and fourth lines:

verso, pp [3–4]; title-page as above, with commercial advertisement on

A final correction can also be made in the publication date of the Adelphi Library edition (2e), which should be 4 November 1908, according to a letter from GM to Emily Lorenz Meyer, and not 'October' as stated on the verso of the title-leaf.

In the entries for *Sister Teresa* (A25) there is listed a 'Trial revised edition' (b) which was known to exist from references to it in several of GM's letters and from a set of proof pages for gathering M (pp 177–92) which were assumed to have been made for this version. A contemporary mention of this 'small edition containing an extra chapter' was in a paragraph under 'Notes of the Day' in *Literature*, 10 August 1901. No copy had been located until recently, but now through the kindness of Alan Rodgers of Carrowdore, County Down, Northern Ireland, definite information about this edition can be recorded. He has in his collection one of the twenty copies issued, a presentation copy to P.T. Gill, which he has made available through photocopies of the entire book. Among the differences from the first edition are the omission of the frontispiece, the insertion of a new four-leaf gathering I2 (pp 144A–144H) between gathering I and K and the reimposition of these two gatherings to accommodate a new chapter XXVI, with the former chapter XXVI now designated XXVIA. Also reimposed is gathering M (noted above) to permit the substitution of new text for old near the beginning of chapter XXXI. These revisions were used by GM for the 'specially rewritten' text of the Tauchnitz edition (2b).

No new titles have come to light in the first section of 'Books and Pamphlets' since the *Bibliography* was published, but a number of new impressions of various titles have been discovered. Four additional 'Colonial' editions have been found, two of them using sheets of discontinued texts. The first of these is *Evelyn Innes*, where sheets of the first edition, cut down and with the first gathering reset were used for Unwin's Colonial Library (a2). Sheets of both the first and second editions of *The Lake* were used in Heinemann's Colonial Library (a2 and b2). The sheets of the withdrawn first edition were used first, and when these were exhausted, sheets of the second were substituted. Outwardly the two editions are identical. The fourth is *Lewis Seymour and Some Women* (A36–2a2) also in the Heinemann Colonial Library.

Plates of three other titles in the Heinemann regular editions were used for special impressions issued on thinner paper, with the title-pages in two colours and in a three-quarter leather binding. These are *Confessions of a Young Man* (A12–2e2a), *Esther Waters* (A19–4c2a), and *The Brook Kerith* (A35–b2a). Apparently these editions were issued for sale in Canada as Toronto has been added to the publisher's imprint on the title-page. Also Heinemann's issued three titles in the Uniform Edition in special bindings for the Times Book Club. These were *The Brook Kerith* (A35–b), *Avowals* (A38–b), and *Celibate Lives* (A52–a).

Additional impressions of some American editions have been located, and one that might be mentioned here is a reissue of *Mike Fletcher* (A14–2a) with an added sub-title, 'The Romance of an Irish Hero,' presumably added to make it more salable to the large number of Americans of recent Irish extraction.

A never reprinted article by GM on the London art scene, 'Memories of '95', has been located in *The Year's Art 1896*, compiled by S.C.R. Carter and published by J.S. Virtue & Co., Ltd., London, 1896. This will now be included as B7+1 in the second section, 'Contributions'.

Other titles may still be found which at present are unrecorded and these will be included, if located in time, in the forthcoming *Supplement*. Many variants have been and are still being discovered, mainly involving binding colours and stampings growing out of the seemingly chaotic publishing practices of the 1880s, '90s and early years of this century.

Among the variants already located is a later impression of the first American printing of *A Modern Lover* (A5–b) which has the postal notice on the title-page omitted. It has been numbered A5–2b+1 and it appears to be a volume in the publisher's 'Popular Series' as its elaborately decorated yellow cloth binding duplicates that of *An Actor's Wife* (A6–2b2), which is identified as being in that series. *An Actor's Wife* is the title used on the early unauthorized editions of *A Mummer's Wife*. Sheets of this impression of *An Actor's Wife*, with a July 1889 date included in the postal notice on the title-page, were also reissued, circa 1892–93, in the 'Columbia Series' and this has been renumbered A6–2b3.

Another binding variant is probably earlier than the one described in the bibliography for the first authorized American edition of *A Mummer's Wife* (3b). It is dark blue cloth, with back cover plain and front cover blind stamped with a single rule border at outer edge. The stamping on the front cover and spine is in gilt. A copy of the first edition of *A Mere Accident* (A10–a), which is owned by an English collector, has the normal blind stamped border on the front cover in brown matching the lettering.

The second impression of the third English edition of *Confessions of a Young Man* (A12–c) was issued in bright red cloth, and copies of this impression were used for the American issue (c2) with a tipped-in slip at the title-page giving the New York publisher's imprint, but at least one copy has been reported with the slip tipped in a copy bound in the green cloth of the first impression.

'Mudie's Select Library' seems to have taken some books in sewn sheets and then, after additional reinforcing, casing them in their own covers. A copy of *Impressions and Opinions* (A15–a), in the library of an American collector, has the cut-down pages cased in dark blue buckram, with a Mudie's label on the front cover, pasted over an earlier label. The sheets are early ones as page number 180 is perfect as found in the first state of the regular edition. The spine is unevenly gilt lettered: MOORE'S/IMPRESSIONS/ETC

Another American collector has a copy of the third [second English] edition of *Vain Fortune* (A16–c) which is a combination of the last two issues, having the illustrations present and the publisher's name at foot of spine as in the second issue, but lacking the advertisements and having the red binding of the third issue.

There are at least two copies of *Celibates* (A21–a) which have white endpapers and the top edges of these are not gilt as are those of the usual dark-blue ones. Also the sheets are not sewn on tapes as are all other copies seen, so it is possible that these were cased hurriedly to supply reviewers with advance copies.

In the bibliography a footnote told of a variant state of the binding of *The Untilled Field* (A26–a), with the author's name in two lines on the spine. Since publication at least three and possibly four copies have been located which are stamped as described and also with the book's title in a single line on the front cover. Oddly enough, and a fact that I failed to note, this variant is the one described by Danielson in his early bibliography.

Two different Colonial editions of *The Lake* (A27) have previously been noted, but there are also two variant bindings of that title which should be mentioned. The first is a copy of the first edition (a) catalogued recently by a New York dealer and since sold to a Japanese dealer. It is bound in green cloth and has the author's name and title stamped within gilt boxes on both the front cover and spine, but there is no publisher's name stamped on the spine, so it appears that the book has been recased at a later date by someone other than the publisher and probably it is not a legitimate binding variant. The other is a copy of the third English edition (d) that has the back cover plain without the publisher's monogram stamped in the lower right corner as is usual. There is also an inserted catalogue of publisher's advertisements inserted at the end, which is not normally included. This is an oddity for it lists, among other books by GM, one unknown to bibliographers and collectors, *The Confessions of a Dead [sic] Man.*

A reviewer of the bibliography noted that *Reminiscenses of the Impressionist Painters* (A28) 'was also issued in plum-coloured wrappers' but no copy so bound has been located. It is not listed by Frances-Jane French in her *A Bibliography of the Tower Press*

Booklets (Athlone, 1968, 25 copies, reprinted from *An Leabharlann*, the journal of the Library Association of Ireland, Vol. 25, No. 4, December 1967). She describes the wrappers as being 'dove grey', but according to her, the preceding volume in the series (*Songs of a Devotee*, by Thomas Koehler) was issued in 'plum wrappers', so it is possible that a small amount of this stock remained and was used for one or more copies of the GM title.

The American issue of *The Apostle* (A30–a2) used sheets of the Dublin edition, but without the final gathering of publisher's advertisements and with a reset title-page with the Boston publisher's name added, and with his name at the foot of the spine. There is at least one mixed copy, with the final gathering of advertisements and the Dublin publisher's imprint on the spine, but with the title-page that includes the American publisher's name in the imprint.

The reviewer cited above also noted that some copies of the first volume of *Hail and Farewell: Ave* (A31:I–a) 'were cased in red cloth for distribution to the circulating libraries.' No copy of this variant has been seen, but it is very likely that if such a binding exists it was also used for the other two volumes of the trilogy.

These, and other variants await further research. Their primary interest is to the collector (and dealer) and they have scant value for the textual scholar, but they are of interest to the student of late-nineteenth- and early-twentieth-century publishing practices.

It is hoped that some scholar, in the not too distant future, will undertake an in-depth study of the binding, stamping, and endpaper variants of publishers of the period, especially Vizetelly, Scott, Unwin, and Heinemann. There seems to be almost countless instances of minute variations within a single edition, impression, or issue. For instance, an English book dealer wrote an American bibliographer, more than thirty years ago, that he had discovered at least five variants or issues of the first edition of *Evelyn Innes*. These may have included the second edition, which had at that time not been identified as a separate issue, but as he declined to answer queries and apparently failed to publish his findings, some of the variants he noted must at present go unrecorded.

To bibliography there is no end. Or, so it seems to at least one bibliographer who has been tracking down trivia regarding GM's books, along with more important details, for nearly five decades. The trivia is in many cases of interest, although not always of real bibliographical importance, but this certainly is not enough reason that the search should not continue.

NOTES ON CONTRIBUTORS

ROBERT STEPHEN BECKER is Assistant Professor of Humanities, Oxford College, Emory University. Formerly a Mellon Fellow at the University of Pittsburgh, Professor Becker is the author of essays concerning George Moore's interest in painting; he also has prepared photographic essays (including the one published in this volume) that are a valuable supplement to biographical studies of Moore. His major work, now in progress, from which his essay comparing the public and private personae of Moore derives, has been the collecting and editing of George Moore's personal and professional correspondence. The first volume of these letters shortly will be published by Colin Smythe Ltd.

RICHARD J. BYRNE, by profession an architectural designer, is known also as a journalist, playwright, musician, actor, and director. Although he has lived and worked in Dublin and Paris, most of his life has been spent in the west of Ireland where he was born and educated, chiefly in Galway and Westport. For many years he was artistic director of Taibhdhearc na Gaillimh. His one-act plays and musicals written for Ireland's Irish language theatre have brought him special acclaim. *Seoda* (jewels), his showcase production that combined traditional Irish music, dance, and drama, was for many years an annual event of the Taibhdhearc. His favourite books by George Moore are those set in Mayo, which he regards as faithful to both the beauty of the countryside and the spirit of its people.

JANE CRISLER combines scholarship in French history of the late nineteenth century at the University of Wisconsin-Madison with administrative work at the University of Wisconsin-Milwaukee. Recently returned from a year's research in Paris, she is especially interested in the Irish colony that developed in the French capital in the last quarter of the nineteenth century and the first quarter of the twentieth, its cultural and intellectual ties with French artists, writers, and political activists, and its roots in earlier Irish and French history. The role of women within the Irish colony in France establishes the compatibility of her secondary interest in women's studies with her other scholarly work.

GARETH W. DUNLEAVY, Professor of English and Comparative Literature at the University of Wisconsin-Milwaukee, is a medievalist with strong interests in the influence of the middle ages on the modern world. Author of *Colum's Other Island* and *Douglas Hyde* and co-author of *The O'Conor Papers*, he has contributed dozens of articles and reviews on Old English elegiac verse, Chaucer, English poetry of the Middle Ages, Irish folklore and folklorists, the cultural milieu of nineteenth-century Ireland, and major figures of the Irish literary renaissance to books and journals. His long interest in George Moore's medievalism began when he first read *Héloïse and Abélard* as a student. A 1984 Guggenheim Fellow, he is now at work, in collaboration with Janet E. Dunleavy, on a definitive biography of Douglas Hyde.

JANET EGLESON DUNLEAVY, Professor of English at the University of Wisconsin-Milwaukee, was first drawn to George Moore through her interest in experimental narrative techniques of prose writers of the nineteenth and twentieth centuries. Her books include *Design for Writing*; *George Moore: The Artist's Vision, The Storyteller's Art*; and an edition of one of Trollope's Irish novels, *Castle Richmond*. She is also co-author of *The O'Conor Papers* and author of essays on George Moore, Mary Lavin, Elizabeth Bowen, Anthony Trollope, James Joyce, W.B. Yeats, Irish folklore, the Irish short story, and the cultural milieu of nineteenth-century Ireland. From 1972 to 1978 she edited *The American Committee for Irish Studies Newsletter*. Her study of Mary Lavin's fiction will appear shortly. A 1984 Guggenheim Fellow, she is now collaborating with Gareth W. Dunleavy on a biography of Douglas Hyde.

MELVIN J. FRIEDMAN is Professor of English and Comparative Literature at the University of Wisconsin-Milwaukee. Widely known for his work in American and continental literature, he is equally at home in Irish studies, as a result of his many publications on Beckett and Joyce. Among his books, *Configuration Critique de Samuel Beckett*, *Samuel Beckett Now*, and *Calepins de Bibliographie Samuel Beckett* are probably best known to specialists in Irish literature. Professor Friedman serves on the boards of *Contemporary Literature*, *Studies in American Fiction*, *Renascence*, *Studies in* the *Novel*, *Journal of Popular Culture*, *Journal of American Culture*, and *Fer de Lance*. He is currently co-editing a collection of essays on the American southern writer, Flannery O'Connor.

EDWIN GILCHER is well-known to a grateful generation of Moore's scholars as the compiler of *A Bibliography of George Moore*, a work that began casually, with the discovery of textual differences in various editions of Moore's books, and took thirty years to complete, for reasons well known to every student of Moore. For each time a new edition of one of Moore's books was published, the author took the opportunity to revise – sometimes noticeably and extensively, sometimes minutely but importantly. Moreover, George Moore published frequently in periodicals in England and Ireland, sometimes anonymously and sometimes under an assumed name. These periodical pieces, as Edwin Gilcher has demonstrated, are also of major importance, for many of them were in fact early drafts of works later published in book form. A tireless investigator, Mr. Gilcher has continued his bibliographic studies since the publication of the *Bibliography*: the first update, including some of his discoveries since 1970, appears in this volume. To collectors of Moore's writings, he speaks with an authority none can match.

JAMES LIDDY divides his time between his duties as Associate Professor of English at the University of Wisconsin-Milwaukee and editor of the *Gorey Detail* and co-coordinator of the Gorey Arts Festival in Ireland. A barrister by training, he turned to writing poetry soon after completing his education. A founding member and editor of *Arena*, he has served also on the editorial boards of *Poetry Ireland* and *Nine Queen Bees*. Among his many books of poetry, *In A Blue Smoke*, *Blue Mountain*, *A Munster Song of Love and War*, and *Corca Bascinn* will be familiar to most readers interested in Irish poetry. He also has published short fiction and critical essays on poetry and on Irish literature. As a scholar, he focusses for the most part on the poetry of the two Irelands, north and south. He is currently at work on a novel.

PATRICK A. MCCARTHY is Associate Professor of English at the University of Miami, where he teaches a wide range of courses in nineteenth- and twentieth-century literature. His scholarly interests are equally broad, but he is best known for his contributions to Irish studies. Among his books are *The Riddles of Finnegans Wake* and *Olaf Stapledon*. His many articles on Joyce,

Yeats, T.S. Eliot, Brendan Behan, and Olaf Stapledon have appeared in a number of professional journals and scholarly books. From 1978 to 1982 Professor McCarthy edited *The American Committee for Irish Studies Newsletter*. He is a member of the Board of Editors of the *Irish Renaissance Annual*. He recently served as Guest Editor of the special Olaf Stapledon issue of *Science-Fiction Studies* (November, 1982).

INDEX